CW00405626

Brighde's Cave

by

Isabella Weber

First published by Zidane Press in 2011.

Zidane Press Ltd.
Unit 4. Olympia Trading Estate
London N22 6TZ

Graphic Design by Em Mathews

Distributed by:
Turnaround Publisher Services Ltd.
Unit 3. Olympia Trading Estate
London N22 6TZ
T: +44 (0)20 8829 3019

British Library Catalogue in Publication data.
A catalogue record for this book is available from the British Library.

ISBN 9780956267825

zidanepress.com

The inspiration came to me in a meditation on Brighde, where I was led into her cave that was enriched with her healing flame, filled with divine crystals and she sat me down and opened pages of a journal and encouraged me to create a story based around the Maiden, Mother and Crone Myth.

This book is dedicated to the lovely memory of my Mother Eliane Barbet; 1934-2010
the most amazing, inspiring loving supportive mother, much cherished and adored.

I'd also like to dedicate and honour this book to my Beloved Aunt Vivianne Szabo 1936-2007. Who was like a mother to me in every way. Thank you Marrianne for all your love that you gave to me and our family. Bless it Be.

Acknowledgements

I would like to thank my beloved partner and soul mate Steve for all his love and support through the writing of this book. My teacher Kathy Jones who is always a great inspiration and source of encouragement, thank you for your support. To my dearest friends Dave and Jill, Laura Holdstock, Sara Hall and all my friends who helped and encouraged me thank you all so much, and to Richard and Em, for all their work in helping to make it all possible. I'd like to extend also a big thank you to Brighde Priestesses Marion, Heather, Moana, Iona, Sarah, and Rita for their contributions and everyone else who has been involved. May you all be blessed with Brighde's light.

Content

Chapter 1

When I dedicated to becoming a Brighde Priestess on Kathy Jones' Brighde Retreat in Glastonbury at Imbolc of 2007 I was unaware of how my journey with her would unfold and the depths that she has taken me to in my own personal healing.

I have found her to not only be a gentle loving companion but always there, full of fire, waiting for me to call her in when I need to.

When I lost my mother in April 2010, Brighde was guiding me with signs before this was going to happen, as at the time I was caring for many friends of mine who had been recently bereaved themselves, little did I know I was next.

During the Brighde Imbolc retreat of 2010, myself and Marion Van Eupen created a healing alter to comfort those who were experiencing loss. Each one of us gathered close and lit a candle to those that needed healing at the time. Many emotional tears were shed. Brighde's healing light was flowing through us, going deep into the darker places inside that needed rekindling and Brighde's warmth. Brighde's fire was present, I felt her so strongly, more that I could have imagined.

What a gift she bestowed on me, it was one of renewal, reawakening an internal life force energy inside me that had been dormant over the winter. I discovered that she has this unique ability to reach inside and transform the deepest part of the self, that had been unreachable. She goes there on your behalf, bringing it to your attention, showing you what you need to change. She did this for me, and I embraced it. It was such a relief to witness my own personal transformation as my painful shadow turned into light and I could let it go and move forward with inner strength. Then I was met by her wonderful animals.

Brighde's wolf, I find, offers me protection and a fierce love and warmth that makes me feel safe and empowered. Then there is her graceful swan, that I call to and find myself wrapped up in her loving swan wings, embracing and nurturing my spirit. I also like her charming snake, that I find brings great healing and change as it teaches me to shed the skin of old patterns that no longer serve me. Not to be forgotten also is Brighde's loving cow with red ears, who is just so gentle and tender providing the nourishing mother's milk, the kind of milk that I have been craving all my life.

All this I have experienced and more since running the Brighde retreat with Marion for the last three years. To me Brighde is continuing to show and teach me about my life and path, not knowing this was possible in becoming her priestess. Not only is she loving, fun and playful, but she is there the whole time, even when I don't know it, holding and supporting me through difficult times. She has a very nice way of showing me how to hang out my dirty washing, that it's okay and not to be ashamed of it but to simply let it go with grace so that I can move forward in my life with her blessing showing me the way.

Brighde comes through in different forms and when I was in Handfasted in a traditional Pagan Wedding ceremony in 2011, she came to me as The Bride, helping me prepare to be a Bride.

The Calling Of Bride Imbolc 2011

Brigit, Brie, Brigantia, Bridie, daughter of February, Goddess of so many names.
I hear your calling Brighde to be your Bride again.

Bless me with your sovereignty, help me to remember your light.

O Shining one, I hear your call to fill myself with your love.

Goddess with your Quickening Rod incarnate my spirit into life!

O Brighde I hear your call through meeting your Maiden wolf.
A tiny beautiful wolf cub that licks and plays with its paws.
It's helping me to awaken my inner child, bless you Brighde.

O Brighde I hear your call through meeting your Lover wolf.
I see before me a strong and sensual male wolf.
He is calling me to him, tantalising me with his passion.

O Brighde I hear your call through meeting your Mother Wolf.
Here she comes, so pure and white as snow.
Her eyes stare straight into mine.
She sees my soul and knows all.

O Brighde I hear your call through meeting your Crone Wolf.
Behind me I turn and there stands an old grey wolf
nuzzling my side with a soft and gentle paw.
She has learnt the gift of love through years of wisdom.
She brings me healing and opens my heart, bless you Brighde.

You have shown me what it means to be a Bride again
To walk beside you with your wolves
Guiding me between the worlds
I understand what it means to be alive again.

May your light shine brightly for ever more.
May your eternal flame rise again and again
helping all who come to journey with you.
Bless you Brighde,
Bless you Ancient Mother Brigantia

How to Connect with Brighde

Brighde is the Ancient Goddess of England where she is celebrated as The Lady of Fire, and of the Sun and the Moon and the Springs and the Wells. She is the strength and power that brings light to the dark places inside our lives. She inspires and transforms us, by challenging us to be true to ourselves. She has the ability to awaken the Alchemy of our Souls. Her healing fires reach our hearts and shows us how to burn through the dross, and clear out the old patterns and ways, so that our soul can come through with more light, bringing gift's of inspiration and creativity.

Brighid is also a Goddess Saint, Maiden, Mother, Crone and Triple Fire Goddess of Fertility, Healing, Generosity, Creativity, Inspiration, Transforming Smithcraft, poetry, spinning, weaving and more. By experiencing all her different aspects, she helps you to open yourself up to Her healing energies and invite the seeds that have been dormant inside of you to awaken by the touch of her quickening rod.

There are many ways you can show your dedication to the Goddess Brighde and to ask her for blessings, protection, and guidance. I have been inspired to share with you the wonderful work of Susa Morgan Black, Scot Druid, OBOD in her work on 'Brigit Patron Goddess Saint.'

You can dedicate a white candle to Brighde and light it whenever you perform a ceremony dedicated to her. Ask her for inspiration in poetry and any kind of artistic endeavour or craft work. You can ask her guidance for healing, and for protection from harm. You can make up your own prayers, by simply asking Brighde to help you with what you need.

You can float 19 small white candles in a bowl at Imbolc on the first of February, to represent Brighde's 19 nuns who maintained her eternal fire in Kildare.

You can hang ribbons or strips of cloth on a tree dedicated to the saint to bless for healing. Her colours are white, red, blue and green.

In a pagan community, Brighid is a significant time for initiation. The Goddess acts as a guide to initiates. If you are a part of an initiatory religion or organization, this is an ideal time to perform the ceremony.

Create your own ritual on Imbolc. Have an intimate party for your family and closest friends. Serve wholesome foods made with milk products. Dedicate a white candle to her and leave it out overnight to be blessed by Brighde. Use that candle for the rest of the year in your Brighde ceremonies.

Make a Brighde's cross, or a corn dolly, dressed in white and place it in a basket bed. Flower shops sell "raffia" by the bundle, which works very well for making a "corn dolly". Be sure to call out, "Bride, thy bed is ready! You can also leave bread and fresh butter on your window sill for her, this is an Irish tradition on St. Brighde's Eve, 31st of January and a little straw or hay for the fairy cow that travels with her on this holy night. This is also a good time to give generously to the poor. Keep a symbol of her (a corn dolly, a

Catholic Saint Brigit statuette, a Brigit's cross) near your hearth, for she is the hearth keeper. If you don't have a hearth, keep it near your stove. Make sure it is safe from the heat! If you are lucky and have a bath, keep a symbol of her nearby, for she is the patroness of healing wells, and baths can be a modern version! Alternatively, some people keep it by their front door, or in the highest corner of their house.

Create a rite of purification in your bathtub. Light white candles and ask the Goddess to bless the water. Let yourself soak in the healing waters and focus on the candle flame while you meditate on her healing qualities. If you have a fireplace, dry off at the hearth, asking for her blessings with the element of fire. She is the Goddess of fire and water, and you have called her in both elements.

Make and dedicate a wand in the service of Brighde. In the legends, she used a white birch or willow wand. She is also associated with oak. You can use this in ceremonies of healing to invoke her guidance. She is said to have owned a white snake, which aided her in healing, and the white wand represents the snake.

In the Celtic legend Brighde wore a green or blue mantle so powerful that it spread itself over Kildare, forcing the king to grant the land to Brighde. Brighde once hung her magical cloak on a sun ray. You can make your own cloak and ask Brighde to bless this sacred cloak to be used for healing. When you see a person who is unwell, you can spread your coat over this person, and send healing prayers to Brighde. Whenever you feel a calling to Brighde to come and be with you, you can wear this cloak and trust that Brighde's spirit is with you.

You can also make a prayer necklace of 19 white beads. The number 19 symbolises the 19 Brighde nuns that stayed with Brighde in her place of worship at Kildare. You can add a special symbol to your necklace that represents Brighde to you – a Brighde's cross, a Catholic Saint Brighde medal, a swan or snake pendant. Use this necklace as a focal point for meditation with Brighde. Keep it with you when you need her inspiration or protection.

You can meditate on Saint Brighde. You can find prayer cards of the Saint in Catholic supply shops.

You can meditate for 19 minutes acknowledging the 19 day cycle of her worship at Kildare.

There are many crafts, talents, and skills that Brighde patronizes. Ale and mead brewing, dying, cloth weaving, wheat weaving, smithcrafting, poetry, singing, harping, agriculture and animal husbandry, divination, midwifery, and healing. Explore these fields as a possible vocation or hobby, and see if it brings you deep satisfaction, with her guidance.

You can also be willing to volunteer your time and resources in her name when she calls you to. Trust the path of service that Brighde opens up to you.

I am offering a one year correspondence training course to become a Priest/Priestess of Brighde. Please see the details of the training in Chapter Five.

Chapter 2

At Home in the Glass Isle

Glastonbury Tor
Image courtesy of Steve Dixson

Far far away, on a beautiful island lived a little girl called Brighde who loved playing with her dolls, and spending time in a special place she called her cave, where magical experiences would happen to her without her really knowing what they meant. It was in that place that she would make contact with a Lady she didn't really know but trusted in her love and guidance believing she was real because she could see her just like she saw the flowers and the trees. That Lady would introduce her to wonderful animals, like her friend Stardust who was an amazing female Unicorn with rainbow colours and a sparkly horn that sprinkled beautiful shimmering star dust everywhere she went. When Brighde asked Stardust what she was doing, Stardust would whisper in her ear that she was sprinkling mother earth with a healing glitter that would help the plants and flowers to grow better. Brighde loved going on journeys with Stardust and playing and having fun, until she would hear her name being called by one of her many sisters to come home.

Brighde was the youngest of five girls, and she remembered her Mother Kerr saying that she was an unexpected bundle of joy and it was her Father Dagda's lust that had kindled her into the world. Mother Kerr was Brighde's idol, she had the most beautiful Golden Hair and deep green eyes that when Brighde looked into them, would fill her with the most enduring love. Brighde would do anything for her mother. She was very affectionate and gave Brighde a lot of attention and care as she felt that Brighde would be something special one day and help other people. Mother Kerr would wake Brighde up early every morning with a gentle kiss on the cheek and take her in her arms and say that it was time to visit the cows and get the milk. Off they would go hand in hand and Mother Kerr would teach Brighde how to milk the cows and hold the udder and squeeze each teet in her hand and out like a spraying waterfall would pour the milk! This would bring Brighde so much joy she felt drawn to the cows and would talk to them and sing them songs. It was in the morning that Mother Kerr would show Brighde how to take the milk and turn in into cream and Brighde would watch mesmerised as the milk would turn and churn around and around and this got Brighde really excited. She felt she could do something more with this skill and help her mother not to work so hard. She could make the cream every morning and help Mother Kerr make butter and with this produce they could give it away to the local village and in exchange Mother Kerr could have more help from the local villagers at home in the farm and would not have to work so hard.

Every morning Brighde would wake up extra early and go and see the cows and start milking them before Mother Kerr would arrive. Brighde had been making the cream and turning the milk into butter. She had produced an amazing amount and Mother Kerr couldn't believe it.

'What are we going to do with all this extra cream and butter Brighde?'

Brighde smiled and replied, 'We are going to give it to the people in the village and help them with this delicious produce. We are going to help the poor people Mother Kerr.'

Mother Kerr's heart was taken so much by Brighde's generosity and her kindness, she was overjoyed and helped Brighde to take the produce into the village. So it happened, that every day Brighde would make the cream and produce the butter and the word began to spread in the local village that there was cream and milk and butter available now. Oh what delicious rich and milky cream it was, that everyone was overjoyed and the cakes would begin to be baked and fruit desserts and hand baked bread, made in a fire oven, would be produced and Mother Kerr was overwhelmed with happiness. She really blossomed as she enjoyed cooking so much and there were many happy days spent in the kitchen. This was how Brighde and Mother Kerr developed a loving and caring relationship and Brighde loved to see her Mother Kerr smile and be happy. Brighde would spend time with her in the kitchen and help her wash up and dry each spoon, knife and fork by hand. Knowing that in every action there was joy in Brighde's heart brought joy to Mother Kerr. Mother Kerr loved being a mother and keeping animals and everyone happy. She had a simple heart and never wanted for anything. She loved her husband and did everything she could do with love to bring up her family and create harmony and love in the home. She had learnt this from her mother, and wished to pass it down to her children. Her mother had taught her how to sew and cook delicious meals. She loved cutting pineapples by hand and creating a beautiful pineapple boat that she filled with vegetables, rice and herbs, as well as seeds that she had harvested from the garden. She also really enjoyed seeing her garden flourish with all the fruit and vegetables. It was this teaching that she gave her daughters, she wanted them to learn the traditional ways, so that one day they too would have children and pass it down to them.

Being the youngest Brighde was also very close to her father and he always called her his little Princess. Together they would look after the land and feed the animals. Father Dagda taught Brighde all about the different qualities each animal had and how important it was to look after them. His special gift was with bringing up wolves and befriending them to be companions to their family, so they would look after their land and keep them safe. At first Brighde was afraid of the wolves as a small child, Father Dagda would help her by introducing her to a wolf cub who was so cute and cuddly that they could play together and still her wolf cub would return to her mother to be fed and nourished at the end of the day. Brighde would spend time as she became more aware and would watch how the wolves would interact and hunt with their pack. At night when she would fall asleep and Mother Kerr would tuck her in with a kiss goodnight she would hear the wolves howling into the night and it would send shivers down her spine. She would then remember her father and how he made her feel safe and soon she would be dreaming about playing with her wolf cub and all her fears would drift away as she slept deeply into the night. Brighde promised herself she wanted to make her father proud and take after him. Father Dagda's profession was as a Blacksmith in the local village, he worked at a forge crafting horse shoes, swords, and all kinds of metal objects, including jewellery and silver blacksmithing. She was in awe one night when she caught her father coming home and spoiling her mother with a beautiful gift of a necklace he had been crafting for weeks by hand He simply grabbed Mother Kerr's hand and there appeared this beautiful handmade silver necklace with a sparkling green and gold stone in the centre. Mother Kerr gasped with joy and hugged and kissed him, showing her love and tenderness to him. Then she took her husband's weary hands and gently wash away all the black dirt and soot from his hard day's work. Brighde dreamed one day she would meet someone just like her father and experience this wonderful love that her parents shared for each other. Father Dagda was a great provider for the family and loved all his girls. Brighde pretended that she was his favourite and even when he was really tired and she could see he needed a rest, she would sing to him and play with his hands and he would smile and give her a cuddle. For Brighde his warm loving cuddles were the best thing in the world.

When her father was away at work and her mother was busy with household chores, Brighde enjoyed spending most of her time wandering around the island and going to visit her favourite place. At this place was a cave that Brighde had discovered accidentally one day whilst she was walking around and exploring different places. This cave was a very sacred place for Brighde and it was here that she began to make her dolls and play with them. One day she discovered whilst she was having a little nap that she would dream about this beautiful Lady who came with rainbows and animals and would talk to Brighde and tell her things about her life and how she could help her mother and her sisters. This Lady came with a gift of a horse with a magical horn, they could play together and this horse became her friend, her name was Stardust. Stardust would take Brighde to visit amazing places in mystical lands and Brighde would be loving every moment of this experience knowing it was real. Somehow she felt she couldn't share it with her sisters or her mother and father as this was just for her, her special place. Suddenly she would wake up and return back to the house to help Mother Kerr with whatever work was needed to be done. Their family lived on a farm and there was a lot to do. All the tasks were shared out equally by her father and it was her mother's joy to feed the animals and prepare breakfast for everyone. Her father would tend to anything in the house that needed mending and then he would get himself ready for work. All of Brighde's sisters helped as well, and everyone had their household duties to help keep the farm running and provide food on the table.

Her eldest sister Bambha was in charge of the vegetable garden, weeding, tending the crops that they were growing and looking after all the fruit trees in the orchard. There was a lot of land and many fields filled with a huge variety of fruit trees. Brighde's favourite was the apple orchard, especially in the spring time when all the apple blossoms came out, it was just so beautiful. She spent many lovely afternoons lying on the grass in a blissed out daze just smelling the delicious fragrance. She was Bamba's little helper and she enjoyed listening to Bambha's great knowledge of the moon and how all the seeds needed to be planted at a certain time. She would help Bambha dig the soil and plant the little seeds and help with the watering. Another favourite place of Brighde's was the herb garden, filled with the most amazing variety of medicinal herbs and other herbs they used for cooking. Mother Kerr would always ask Brighde to pick a certain herb for dinner. Brighde would try to remember what her Mother told her and go and pick the herb herself, only to arrive later in the kitchen and hear her Mother say,

'Dear Brighde, you have picked sage instead of rosemary.'

Then she would give her a warm hug and ask Brighde to get her older sister Bambha to show her where the rosemary bush was. This way Brighde would learn about all the herbs and which ones were good for cooking, and which ones were used for medicinal purposes. When Bambha had time she would teach Brighde all about the herbs, fruits and vegetables and as Brighde got older she got better at picking herbs and pleasing her mother with only one trip to the herb garden.

The island was paradise, filled with abundance and all they needed to survive happily. Brighde and her sisters were free to grow up in harmony with mother earth and her animals. The island was a big place and they had little stone walls around their farmland that Brighde's father had built many years ago to make sure that their family home was safe and that the animals knew which pastures to graze in. He had built their home and helped them become self sufficient so they wouldn't need to go outside of the island to earn a living. Brighde was always intrigued about what land was across the water and knew that one day she would find out. Meanwhile she enjoyed her daily chores of helping her sisters and playing in her cave when no one noticed. She also enjoyed visiting Grandmother Kerridyn who lived in her own special house just behind their main house. All her other sisters were scared of bothering Grandma Kerridyn and would say to her,

'Don't go over to Grandma unless she calls you, you'll disturb her and she won't like it! She's always muttering and busy mixing one of her latest potions.'

Brighde would nod politely back to her sisters and say, 'Don't worry I won't disturb her I just like to watch what she's doing!'

Secretly Brighde knew that Grandma Kerridyn was actually really nice and loved her very much, just like she loved her Mother Kerr. Every time she visited Grandma Kerridyn she would welcome her with a lovely delicious drink of some kind that she had just been mixing up. Brighde happily drank it down and would find herself laughing and giggling with Grandma as she told her all these tales of the past and kept her in stitches for hours. Then Grandma would stop just like that and give Brighde a special task that she had to go to some place on the island and wait three days until she could find a certain animal. Her task this time was to find a white sow. Brighde would have to give the white sow special food to eat and talk to it lovingly, then somehow the sow would speak back to her and point at something with her snout and Brighde would find a strange herb to bring back to Grandma Kerridyn. When Brighde returned Grandma Kerridyn was overjoyed with Brighde's find.

'Bless you my child,' she would say, 'you are going to be something special when you grow up, now run along dear and help your mother.'

Brighde loved her mother so much, she had the most beautiful loving heart and would always be smiling and singing most of the time. She was always busy and up to something, whether it was trying a new recipe in the kitchen, cleaning their big family home, washing all the clothes and doing laundry or feeding the birds, she never complained. She was full of love and affection for all the girls even when sometimes they didn't get along, she would sit her sisters down and help them work through their differences. After Bamba, her mother gave birth to Domnu who was such a loving and gentle soul, filled with life's great passion for water, she only wore blue colours and would long to be by the ocean. This was all that Domnu dreamed about and she was often found at the edge of the great lake, soaking wet as she had immersed herself in the water. She would talk about how she had met this amazing dolphin or how she had spoken to some whales who had a message for her. Domnu was deeply passionate about the health of water and how important it was that it was purified and respected, sometimes she would burst out crying saying that mother earth's waters weren't being respected; that fish were dying and she would need to do some work. None of the girls really understood what she was talking about but Mother Kerr would encourage her and look after her each time she came back from being in the water. She would be very cold and Mother Kerr would warm her up by their big fire and help her to feel good about herself. Sometimes Domnu would end up in a fight with her younger sister Arta, who was two years older than Brighde and would pick on Domnu because she liked to challenge others to speak their truth and get in touch with their fiery emotions. Domnu would always end up bursting into tears, leaving Mother Kerr to sit them both down and teach Arta how to channel her built up anger in a more positive and loving manner and not pick on someone she knew would not be able to handle her challenging ways. Arta would get frustrated and scream and shout and stomp outside, she had a lot of power and was very strong willed and knew she had a mission in life that was unstoppable. Mother Kerr knew this and wanted to teach Arta positive creative ways of channelling her powerful emotions. This she did by seeking advice from her Great Aunt Danu who was an incredible astrologer and knew the ways of the ancestors. Great Aunt Danu told her that she should pray to the great Bear Mother who would one day come to Arta in a dream and reveal her true self. Arta would then suddenly change and become very positive and full of enthusiasm for life, she would bring the gifts of the spring time and help the earth to blossom. Mother Kerr prayed that that day would soon come and Arta would mature emotionally and become the daughter she knew she could be.

Brighde watched her sisters grow up and began to notice herself that her body was changing. One sultry sunny afternoon Brighde was out with her closest sister Rhiannon, who was always parading around the house semi-naked . When the sun came out in the sky in the heat of summer Rhiannon would throw her clothes off and lie on the soft green grass sunbathing. Rhiannon liked to teach her sisters how to horse ride in her own time. Now she had plans on teaching Brighde how to ride her horse, but first she just had to sunbathe. Once she was nicely tanned she would call her gorgeous loving mares to her side and introduce Brighde to one that would be easy for Brighde to ride. Suddenly Brighde could feel something happening to her and shouted,

'Rhiannon I am bleeding!' Brighde started breathing heavily and got herself in a complete panic and became very upset. Instantly Rhiannon was by her side hugging and soothing her tears, explaining to Brighde she had entered her moon time, a sacred time of menstruation and that it was time for Brighde's first initiation ceremony into womanhood.

Rhiannon quickly pulled some clothes on and ran back to the house, shouting and screaming 'Brighde's entered her moon time, Brighde's entered her moon time!'

Mother Kerr was overjoyed at the news and asked Rhiannon to teach Brighde how to look after herself with the help of a special moon cup as she was busy beginning to prepare special food and herbs for

Brighde to have that night. Now was the time for Brighde to enter the sacred healing tent where each sister would go, when it was their moon time and be looked after by another sister and Mother Kerr when she had the time.

That night was the full moon and all the sisters and Mother Kerr gathered together and formed a circle outside in the moon light, welcoming Brighde into womanhood. Bambha blessed her with the gifts of mother earth, anointing her feet and body with blessed earth she had gathered from the vegetable garden, to keep her grounded and in touch with the elements of nature. Brighde was smiling and giggling overjoyed at all the attention and so grateful to all her sisters and especially her mother for such love. Next came her sister Domnu who held a chalice and asked Brighde to drink from the holy waters and feel the energy of her womb, awakening her sacred waters, blessing her with great strength during her moon time. Brighde could feel the healing waters soothing her emotions and awakening her womb.

'Thank you sister Domnu.' She embraced her sister with love.

Now Arta stepped forward with a red candle and glowing flame moving the flame around Brighde and then coming back to her womb.

'Feel the warmth of the fires in your belly, may you always be blessed with healing light'. In that second Brighde felt a rising flame burn through her whole being, something magical had happened that she couldn't explain, she felt her heart just wanted to burst open and the palms of her hands were sweating.

'Thank you Sister Arta,' she said, giving her sister a huge warm hug. 'May your fires always burn brightly in you too' she whispered back into Arta's ears and stepped back into the centre of the circle.

Then, surprise surprise, came her Great Aunt Danu in a cloud of smoke, she surrounded Brighde with a blessing of air. She held a huge shell in one hand that contained a burning charcoal which she had sprinkled with special herbs that smelt amazing. Brighde breathed them into her body opening her lungs and releasing sounds from her mouth that she couldn't control.

'Let it out dear one.' her Great Aunt Danu whispered, and on that note Brighde felt all this pent up pain inside of her from when she was smaller come out in this huge sound that took everybody by surprise at first and then everyone joined in and sounded too and these sounds travelled out into the sky and travelled where they needed to go around mother earth. Then her sister Rhiannon started dancing around her, singing and letting off these shrill sounds in high pitches.

'Come on Brighde let yourself go! Dance and move your body like you never done before!'

Brighde was mesmerised by Rhiannon's confidence and the way she moved, she just couldn't believe it was possible but she tried and looked to Rhiannon for encouragement and started to shake her body.

'This is so much fun, I love this, this is great!'

All the sisters were clapping and joining in and Bambha found her drum and joined in with some drumming it was really taking off in some uncontrolled spiral. Then they all collapsed on the ground laughing together in one huge heap.

'Brighde, Brighde!' Mother Kerr broke the laughter with the sounding of her name, Mother Kerr had the most incredible voice that melted Brighde's heart instantly. Brighde came straight away to her mother's side and kneeled in front of her, holding her hands as Mother Kerr sang sweetly and softly repeating Brighde's name. Brighde kneeled in front of Mother Kerr as she placed her hands on Brighde's head and brought through a sacred blessing for her.

'Brighde you are the light, the inspiration in our hearts, you have the gifts of creativity and healing within. Poetry is your mantle, may your poems bring light to all those who hear it. There is great fire and transformation within you, the gifts of smith craft and initiation, quickening and awakening. You were born at the time of Imbolc, you carry the dormant seeds of life and awaken them you will. You carry that spark of life that comes through the earth when the light returns. Bless you my child, much more lies ahead for you my beautiful daughter may you always fulfil your heart's desires.'

Mother Kerr embraced Brighde and soothed her spirit hugging her deeply and filling her with love. Surprise surprise, Father Dagda appeared next to Mother Kerr and gave Brighde a huge warm hug.

As he hugged her he whispered in her ear,

'Remember the spirit of your wolf cub and may she protect you always. Look to the land and the animals for guidance. The beautiful graceful swans that swim softly in our lake, may they help you become you who are. Don't forget our warm giving cows that provide so much milk, good food and nurturing for us all. Then there is what's hidden in the caves, the snake!' With the jolt of a louder tone Brighde jumped out of fear.

'Don't be sacred my child, here is a gift to help you.' He then produced a white hand carved snake made form birch wood, it was like a magical wand.

'Oh this is so beautiful Father' Brighde cried. Everyone gasped with joy and praised their father for producing such a special gift for Brighde. Brighde was in an altered state of consciousness, overwhelmed with all the love and blessings from her family. She didn't really understand the depths of what had been said to her that evening. For her it had been such an incredible moment she breathed it all in and everything was starting to swirl around her. All she knew was that she loved her mother, her father and her sisters so much, this was such a gift, she was completely blown away by it all.

'Thank you Mother Kerr,' she whispered, 'I love you so much,' and sobbed quietly. 'Thank you Father Dagda you are the best! I love you so much too.'

Just when she thought it was all over Grandmother Kerridyn appeared with a special pouch in her hand. Coaxing little Brighde to come over when she was ready, she didn't want to let go of Mother Kerr and Father Dagda's hugs, she loved them both so much. Mother Kerr heard the tone of Grandmother Kerridyn and gently nudged Brighde to let her know it was okay to go over to her grandmother. Brighde breathed deeply, gathered all her strength and moved on to greet her beloved grandma.

'Sweet little Brighde, open your hands I have a precious gift I wish to bestow you.' she said in her husky voice. Brighde opened her hands and Grandma Kerridyn placed a black velvet pouch into her palms. 'Open it! This is a gift that marks your journey into womanhood, may you always remember the innocence of your childhood.' Brighde excitedly opened the black velvet pouch and out came a beautiful necklace with a totem female goddess symbol that was carved out of wood with a spiral on her belly.

'Oh this is beautiful Grandma Kerridyn, thank you, I really love it so much. Thank you so much!' and she hugged Grandma Kerridyn's big body as well as she could and gave her a kiss on her cheek. 'It's really beautiful I love it! Grandma, thank you again and thank you everyone.' she said.

All her sisters, Mother Kerr & Father Dagda joined Brighde in one big family hug and before they knew it they could hear the sounds of the rooster and the first rays of sunshine streaming down from the sky. They had been going all night.

Mother Kerr gathered herself and clapped three times. 'Off to bed everyone, rest day tomorrow! Rhiannon please show Brighde the ways to look after herself during moon time, thank you to all my beautiful daughters and for all your love and kindness that you have shown Brighde this special night. May you all be blessed by the Great Mother herself. Goodnight!'

With that everyone gathered themselves and wandered back to the house. Rhiannon took Brighde to the healing tent where there were hot water bottles in sheep skin, lovely candles and sweet treats in case she was hungry. Rhiannon gave Brighde a decorated book that all the sisters had made together for Brighde's journal so she could write down her dreams and anything that she wished to whilst her moon time was taking place. Brighde was in heaven, she was so filled with all the nights excitement and all the gifts that she had received from her sisters, mother, father and grandma. She prayed to the Lady that she would sleep a sweet night and recover herself the next day.

Brighde's Cave

It was a bright sunny morning and Brighde had been up early milking the cows and churning the butter. She was having a good time singing to the cows and the milk was pouring out into her bucket. Today she had an extra spring in her step and could feel that something magical was going to happen. Her cream production was better than ever and when Mother Kerr arrived she couldn't believe her eyes. She gave Brighde a huge hug and said,

'Brighde you are just getting better and better what's happening my sweet?'

'I am in love and something is taking me over. I don't know, we'll have to wait and see!' With that Brighde gave Mother Kerr the biggest hug ever. 'I'll always be with you wherever you are.'

'What is that suppose to mean Brighde?' Mother Kerr replied knowing that somehow Brighde was up to something, she couldn't put her finger on what it was. She was really grown up now and was an attractive strong young lady with her own mind. Mother Kerr trusted Brighde and knew that whatever happened Brighde would always be okay as she was looked after.

After a delicious breakfast of fresh fruit and scrambled eggs on toast, Brighde set off for the cave. She had her favourite doll Sanya with her, all dressed in white with red hair and decorated bracelets and necklaces, off she went. She didn't say goodbye to her sisters, she didn't want them to know the secret location of her cave.

Bambha was there in the vegetable garden, as Brighde walked by she waved a warm friendly wave and said, 'Have a great day Bambha.' and continued to stroll along.

Somehow she knew she needed to visit Grandmother Kerridyn before she went to the cave as she was wearing her special goddess necklace that she had been given by her at her first moon time ceremony. This had made such a huge impression on Brighde that she would always remember that night and all the kindness and love from all her sisters and her mother and father, she was so grateful to have such a loving and warm family, she really felt blessed.

Grandmother Kerridyn's house was behind the main house down a small beaten track that was covered by huge green ferns that you had to bend back to get through the narrow walk way. Brighde knocked on the wooden door three times, that was her special code and there was Grandma opening the door to meet her. Grandmother Kerridyn had long, white-grey hair that she tied in a bun, she always wore a huge crystal stone around her neck and would be covered in markings. She called them tattoos and had them on her arms and on her back as well. They symbolised rites of passage and entry into other worlds. Today she wore a hand woven dress that was black but had silver and red star patterns all over it. Her small house was like an enchanted earth cave, wall to wall filled with jars full of herbs. There were tall black and red candles burning on the table and many paintings of female forms decorated in stunning earth colours. These paintings, she said, were the memories of the ancestors. Right in the centre of her home was a hot fire burning with a big round cauldron.

'Patience Brighde, you are getting taller than me now my little one, how can this be?' crackled Grandma Kerridyn.

'I am getting older, growing up I think they call it. Something told me I needed to see you today, that you would have something for me.'

'Yes you are right my little one, I have seen the signs and I have been preparing a brew for you to drink, destiny is calling you and there are many changes ahead. Let us see what the spirits wish to tell us today. Drink up my child and come over to the cauldron.' Grandma Kerridyn handed Brighde an old clay cup that was sizzling with some kind of herbal drink. Brighde took the cup and began to drink the herbs, the taste was horrendous but Brighde knew she had to drink it. As she finished the cup she began to feel dizzy and faint. 'Don't worry my little one, come over here and hold my hand.' Brighde did just that and she began to look down into the cauldron. 'Look into the water my dear and tell me what you see in the reflection.'

Brighde looked down into the water and began to see the water moving and then images started to appear. She saw herself running and laughing, playing around and then she saw herself older and fat not knowing that that was an image of her pregnant.

'Tell me what you see little one, as you see them.' Grandmother Kerridyn beckoned. Brighde began to describe the images, not understanding what she saw, but Grandmother Kerridyn knew what she was seeing, she was gifted with the sight and had more abilities than Brighde in seeing the future. 'Look now for Mother Kerr, what do you see?'

'I see Mother Kerr riding on a horse with my sister Rhiannon, she is worried and stressed, something has happened to Father Dagda. They are riding very fast Rhiannon is going faster than Mother Kerr, Mother Kerr is trying to catch up but she is not looking, Oh No!' Brighde shouts, and begins to cry

'Mother Kerr! Mother Kerr!' Brighde is wailing now uncontrollably. Grandmother Kerridyn waits patiently and then she sees what she doesn't want to see, an image of Mother Kerr fallen badly, and her spirit leaving her body. She gasps and takes Brighde in her arms and calms her down,

'There there, don't worry everything is going to be okay, don't worry my little one, everything is going to be okay.' She wraps Brighde in a warm blanket and lies her down, singing her gently to sleep, as Brighde drifts into the dream world.

When Brighde wakes up, Grandmother Kerridyn is nowhere to be seen. She has no memory what so ever of what just happened, she simply felt her head was quite heavy but she was glad she had rested and knew that now she needed to get to the cave. To thank Grandma Kerridyn she left her favourite doll Sonya and looked for a flower from outside in the garden to add to her favourite doll to say thank you. Then she carefully closed the heavy wooden door behind her and made her way down the path under the ferns and into the garden. The sun was shining high in the sky, she realised she must have been out for a few good hours. She was thinking to herself how beautiful wise Grandma Kerridyn was and how she wanted to be like her and have that kind of wisdom and knowledge. As she was wandering along the garden she found her hidden track and felt her heart beat quicker, her cave was approaching. She could see the entrance this time and along the way she had gathered herbs and flowers to bring offerings to the magical Lady that she knew was her special friend. She couldn't wait to play with Stardust and go travelling to other realms.

There it was, the edge of the cave was hidden by this huge reddish-brown rock and in she went happy to see that her other dolls were still there with some rocks and crystals she had gathered. There was also a pile of shells which she was surprised to see. How did they get there she wondered? Could Domnu her sister possibly know about this secret place? 'Impossible.' she thought. Maybe it was a gift from the Lady, she convinced herself that that was probably what it was, picked up the shells and held them close to her ears. She could hear the sounds of the ocean of waves gently crashing, oh how the sound was soothing to her ears and she sat quietly just listening to the shells. This took her far far away into a dream land of the paradise island and she began to crawl on all fours and allowed herself to be guided by the beautiful sounds of the waves. Before she knew it she had come to the edge of a huge tunnel and as she wasn't looking suddenly, bang! She went over the edge and fell into a rush of water that dropped very low. She was choking and fighting for her life, struggling to float and keep on top of the water. The current was so strong that she had no other choice but to continue to go with the flow of the water and try and keep afloat.

It was a struggle but Brighde continued to stay afloat and kept on moving down the stream until, whoosh! She came out into a huge lake and it was dark and Brighde started to feel cold and scared; she was running out of energy and praying to the Lady that she was going to be okay. She kept kicking and struggling in the water. She became surrounded by mists and couldn't see anything at all. All she could do was simply lie on her back and try and stay calm and still as the tidal waters moved her body through the mists and into the night, into the black darkness. Brighde imagined herself in her mother's arms and knew that her mother's love would keep her safe. Suddenly there was a bright light and there were voies calling,

'Is anyone there?' All Brighde could muster were a few splashes. She felt some warm hands pull her up and wrap her in a warm blanket, that was when she passed out.

When she came to, she was suddenly shocked as she felt her body in different clothes and in a completely different place.

'Where am I?' she turned and there was a gentle, handsome, young man smiling at her.

'You are lucky to be alive you know that? What were you doing all out there in the lake on your own? We thought you were dead, my father and I were out fishing. There you were lying in the water, we couldn't believe it, that you were still alive!'

'I don't remember how I got out there, all I remember is that I fell down this huge tunnel that was filled with water and then whoosh, I was suddenly fighting for my life trying to keep alive and survive. Then I was surrounded by mists and I couldn't see anything, I was scared and I didn't know what to do, I prayed and thought of my Mother Kerr and then I felt hands pulling me out of the water. I couldn't believe my eyes, thank you so much, I am so grateful to you and your father. How can I repay you for saving my life?'

'You can stay with us for a little while, I lost my mother when I was born, my father has brought me up completely on his own. We are fisherman and I learnt silver blacksmithing at school.'

'Then you must know my father Dagda, he runs a local silversmith business in the village.'

'That must be another village, we have never come across that village, we don't know that one.'

How was Brighde going to get back home to her family to let her Mother know that she was okay? She didn't have a clue where she was, or how to get back.

'I need some time to think this through.'

'No problem. You can stay here and have a rest and let us know what you'd like to do. My name is Charlie what's yours?'

'My name is Brighde.'

From that day Brighde let go of her life with her family on the island, she had no way of going back and finding where Mother Kerr and Father Dagda lived and so she began a new life with Charlie. They woke up early every morning to go fishing on the lake. They would sit and wait on the boat and Brighde would talk to them about her life on the island and how special her Mother Kerr and Father Dagda were, as well as all her sisters. She learnt how to fish and then how to sell the fish at the market. After they had been to the market, they would go home and Brighde and Charlie's father would make a delicious lunch together. Charlie's father had a very good sense of humour and would make jokes with Brighde and talk about the old days and what life was like growing up in a fishing village and learning from his father. Brighde would then spend the afternoon with Charlie who had an amazing gift with words. Brighde would take these words and turn them into poems that she enjoyed rehearsing in the evening in front of Charlie and his father.

'What an incredible gift you have for reciting poetry, I really feel like I am there with you in every word.' Charlie would gaze into Brighde's eyes and Brighde felt herself blushing, she had never experienced this before. Could Charlie have feelings for her? She didn't understand love and how it was to happen. She only knew what a beautiful relationship Mother Kerr and Father Dagda had together and how much she wanted this for herself too. Little did she know that Charlie really did have feelings for Brighde and something special was about to happen between them.

Back home on the island the sun was setting and a deep red glow was spreading in the sky all over the island. It was going to be a hot day tomorrow. Father Dagda was on his way home carrying the tools he used on his back. A blue and black butterfly flew right in front of him and he was taken aback. This is a message he thought, what could be happening at the farm. He hoped Mother Kerr and the girls were okay. He was looking forward to sharing his tales of the day with Brighde and hugging her a huge warm hug and all his other girls as well. He was getting closer now to home and he could hear that the wolves were restless and needing his attention. He went over to the enclosure and called to the mother wolf to come and see him. She came over quietly to him, she was incredibly striking with a golden shaggy fur coat and stunning green eyes. She howled a strong howl and licked his face. Father Dagda knew that something was up. Someone had left the island otherwise Mother Wolf wouldn't behave like that, she was trying to give him a message.

'What is it Mishka what's happened?'

'Brrrrr,' she sounded, 'brrrr!' Father Dagda looked deeply into her eyes and as he did she guided him to see a vision of a cave and then he saw his youngest daughter Brighde falling down shouting and struggling and then the vision was gone just like that! Father Dagda gave Mishka Mother Wolf a huge huge hug thank you as he squeezed her tight,

'Thank you for showing me Brighde and what has happened to her.'

He nuzzled her nose up against his nose like an Eskimo kiss, it was their special connection and then Mishka pulled away and off she went running quickly back into the wild forest that Father Dagda had helped create for her and her family.

Father Dagda burst into the house and everyone was seated down together including Grandma Kerridyn. Mother Kerr came up to Father Dagda and embraced him strongly. He could tell she had been crying heavily and this was very hard for her. All he did was whisper in her ear.

'It's Brighde, I know she's gone, Mother Wolf Mishka showed me in a vision. It's going to be okay, we both knew from the day Brighde was born that she had a special destiny of her own that we would not be able to control, that all we could do was love her as much as we could for as long as we could.'

With those words Mother Kerr cried some more and Father Dagda hugged her even deeper.

'Let's do a special ceremony tonight to honour Brighde, our shining light and source of love and strength. Girls and Grandma Kerridyn let us make a meal that was Brighde's favourite.'

'I know,' squealed Rhiannon, 'she loved vegetable soup and BBQ corn with Tempeh chips!'

'That sounds great.'

So all the girls and Mother Kerr were busy in the kitchen washing and chopping vegetables. Bambha was busy walking back to the fields with Father Dagda in a state of shock to pick the ripe sweetcorn that would be used for dinner.

'How is this possible Father Dagda, that Brighde can disappear just like that!'

'She hasn't disappear my sweet one Bambha, she has crossed over to the other world, a place that Mother Kerr and I promised we would never share with you girls. We wanted to keep you safe and bring you up in Paradise. Here we would live in peace and harmony and all your needs would be taken care of. We wanted there to be fresh water and plenty of fruit and vegetables, that the soil would be rich with minerals and we would not need or want for anything else.'

'That is how I feel Father, I truly am fulfilled living my life here on the farm and looking after the crops, the trees and the fruit and vegetables. My home is with the earth and I am so happy, I would not want for anything else.'

'That, my sweetest Bambha, makes my heart sing!' As he hugged her deeply and held her hand little tears were streaming down Father Dagda's face as the thought of Brighde and how this had come about was beyond his control. He realised that destiny was something much greater than him and that everyone had their calling in life. Maybe it was Brighde's time, that he had fulfilled his role as a father and Brighde was ready to start her new life on her own. This was the only way he could look at it. Tonight in the ceremony he would pray to the Lady and pray for Brighde's life, that whatever happened, this was what was meant to be and he must be happy that it had come about and be strong for Mother Kerr as she was suffering.

Bambha and Father Dagda collected a huge bunch of ripe golden corn and brought it back to the house, to the great joy of the girls and Mother Kerr.

'Let's build a huge BBQ fire together' bellowed Arta and out she went into the back garden where she had already collected a big pile of fire wood and began scratching sticks together to form a spark. She had a natural ability to start a fire and before she knew it the first spark had activated and the fire was alight and crackling. Domnu heard the sounds from the kitchen and clapped out loud.

'Arta has done it again! Another great fire is on the way!' she loved praising her sister and giving her confidence, even though Arta had continued to bully her all through her early childhood and even now and again as young adults she would do it, but this time, there was a wink that came with it, so she knew she was only kidding. Domnu had the biggest heart, she was so full of compassion and love for all her sisters and every day she would go to the lake and pray and make blessings for her sister and for her mother and father. Grandma Kerridyn knew that Domnu would be given a vision tonight in the ceremony and would be gifted with a message about Brighde. She had been restless all day, knowing that something was up, since Brighde had visited her and had that vision that she had seen of Mother Kerr. She could not share this with anyone she knew, but somehow she trusted that there was a greater presence at hand and that Brighde was following her destiny and there was nothing that anyone could do to bring her back. Grandma Kerridyn had the gift of sight and Brighde had it too but she didn't know yet how to nurture and grow it. Domnu, she knew had the gift of sight too, and there was less fear and more trust, as her connection with water released all her emotions and helped her to feel safe.

Dinner was now cooked and the table was dressed with beautiful decorations, candles were lit and everyone held hands around the table. Mother Kerr gave a blessing of thanks out loud and said a prayer for Brighde that the Lady would keep her safe and bring great blessings to the outside world and that all those who came her way would be touched by her presence.

Brighde's New Life

That night when Brighde went to sleep, she had the most incredible dream. She dreamt that Mother Kerr, Father Dagda and all her sisters were saying how much they loved her and how special she was. She even saw Grandmother Kerridyn giving her a blessing and asking her to look after herself and take care. She woke up the next morning feeling so much love it was just amazing. Charlie noticed Brighde's feelings and said,

'You are glowing Brighde, what's happened to you?'

'I have just had the most amazing dream from my family, they were all thinking of me and sending me love. Somehow we are all connected, it's so special. I so wish you could meet them. You would love my father Dagda, he is just the most down to earth and gifted man you can imagine!'

'So now I know who takes after her father.'

'And my mother as well, she is so beautiful and loving and creative, she knows exactly what you need to feel good. She is really just the best mother I could have dreamed of, really, I really mean it.'

'She sounds really special, I would love to meet your family, maybe one day it will be possible.'

'We could try and go in the boat and see what happens, I am sure we can't be that far away. I got here somehow, you must remember how you picked me up from the water.'

'Yes, I remember where my father led me on the boat, we had never gone that far before. It's somewhere we are are not familiar with. I'll ask my father and see what he can do. We have to catch a lot of fish first to raise enough money to be able to be free for a few days or a week, if we are gone that long. I need to make sure my father is going to be okay.'

That was enough for Brighde to be truly happy, just to know that she had that hope of reuniting with her family, that there was a possibility that it could happen at some point. With that she gave Charlie the biggest hug he had ever received from her and suddenly they looked into each others eyes and he lent over to her and pressed his lips on her lips and they embraced in a deep passionate embrace and before she knew it Charlie and her were overtaken by an incredible desire to touch each other and explore each other's bodies with a wildness that Brighde had never experienced before. Brighde had a sudden flash of her sister Rhiannon who loved her body and would always run around topless and expose her self in the most outrageous way.

'Here is to you Rhiannon' Brighde thought as an uncontrollable passion took over and their two bodies united in waves of loving ecstasy. They made out and just couldn't stop themselves from touching each other and kissing and caressing and loving in the most deepest and beautiful raw way. How much they had been controlling and holding themselves back and for Brighde this was her first love, she was nervous. The whole time Charlie would caress her and go slowly, whispering sweet nothings in her ear, kissing her neck, which would excite her even more. She felt all her nerves and tension releasing and enjoyed kissing him tremendously and holding him as he touched her breasts and explored her body in ways that she had never imagined. When her hymen broke it was so gentle she didn't really notice it as she was so aroused by that point. She had entered another world of bliss and was so happy and overjoyed that Charlie felt this way about her.

From that moment on the two of them fell totally in love and couldn't help touching each other and kissing and playing. Every day was a new experience as they tried different positions and both became more confident and understood what the other liked and didn't like. They were totally smitten on each other, completely forgetting the nature of creation. Until two months had passed and Brighde was cooking Charlie and his father's dinner, she was feeling pretty excited as she was just so in love, everything was wonderful. She spent her days creating a lovely vegetable patch in the garden next to their cottage, she had found the local market and had started decorating and furnishing the home with her own unique style. Both Charlie and his father welcomed Brighde and made her feel at home. Brighde and Charlie both loved cooking and nurturing touch and were so happy that there was a really beautiful love blossoming between them. Charlie's father could see this and had a little pep talk with Charlie, preparing him for what one day may happen. He warned that if the both of them weren't careful, they might have a baby on the way and that it would be a big change. Charlie hadn't thought of this at all, he was so in love with Brighde; her beautiful green eyes, soft pale skin and glowing red hair, that this was the last thing that had crossed his mind. He told his father he would talk to Brighde tonight and see how they could be more cautious and time their playful loving around Brighde's cycles.

When they arrived home, Brighde had created a feast. The dinner table looked stunning, with white candles and flowers and an arrangement of natural shells which Brighde had collected and made into a beautiful table decoration.

'Wow!' Charlie beamed when they got home. 'What's the occasion my darling?'

'I just wanted to celebrate how happy I am with you, now that it's been two months in love and six months since I arrived. It has been such an intense and simply wonderful time, I just wanted to celebrate with you both and thank you Charlie and Father for looking after me and taking care of me so well.'

'You are very welcome both of you,' said Charlie's father. 'It was such a miracle when we found you, we just couldn't believe you were alive! We are just so happy and blessed to have you.'

'Thank you both once more from the bottom of my heart and to that I propose a toast for our future love together.' Brighde lifted her glass and Charlie and his father joined in and they ate and sang and made jokes and laughed through the whole dinner.

Later on that night when Charlie and Brighde were in bed together kissing and caressing, Charlie ran his hand over Brighde's flat tummy, and said,

'We need to be careful, you know what I mean?'

'Oh yes sweety, oh yes, about having a baby. I just thought about that today and was planning on telling you tonight. Actually I haven't had my period for the last month, maybe it's late I don't know, I lost count I was totally carried away by you and our special love, it totally didn't cross my mind.'

'Yes me too my sweet, but my father said to me today to be careful as we don't have that much, I don't know how we could bring up a child here. There is not much future here, you know.'

'Yes I know, which is why we must try and go back to the island where my beloved Mother Kerr and Father Dagda are, so that Father Dagda can take you on in his blacksmith workshop. There is plenty of food, we will not have to worry about a thing.'

With that that Brighde tenderly kissed his lips and again their passion was so strong they united in a loving embrace and all was forgotten.

A few more months passed and Brighde realised now that she was pregnant and even though she didn't show that much yet, she could feel her clothes getting tighter and her breasts getting bigger, she was sick some mornings. Luckily Charlie and his father were up early most mornings and made their own breakfast and were out on the boat for most of the day, coming home in the afternoons. Brighde had some cloth left and altered her clothes to make it appear like everything was normal and she was covering up her weight gain. That night Charlie couldn't help but notice.

'Brighde, look at you, your breasts are so much bigger, they must be, and your flat stomach which I totally adore, is no longer. Darling is it real? Are you pregnant with our child? If this is true I am so happy I can't believe it has happened. I know my father won't be happy, as you say maybe we can try and find your island and everything will be okay!'

'Oh I was so hoping you would say that!' I don't know how but this baby has happened, and it must be a celebration of our love together. It's a gift and I am so sure that when it's the right time we will go to the island and find my home. We must plan it as I can not cover up for much longer. My body is changing and I can't help it, I am going to get bigger in the next few months and your father will notice for sure.'

'Don't worry about my father I will handle him, I feel he won't want to come with us, he will stay here, it is his home and he is happy here. I think he will want a new future for both of us and he will be okay with it. Let me talk to him tomorrow and we will go from there.'

Brighde gave Charlie a huge loving squeeze, she could not believe what he just said. It was a dream come true, she knew it was possible somehow. 'The Lady will help us, I know she will.'

She prayed to the Lady, her Mother Kerr, Father Dagda, Grandmother Kerridyn and all her sisters, she asked for their help in bringing her back home to the island. May she give her a sign? Something that would help them both to come home. Brighde slept a fairly restless night, with dreams of being in the ocean and drowning and all kinds of fears surfacing. She needed to get up and go to the toilet to pee, this only started happening in the last few nights as she could feel her stomach and the baby starting to move, she must be five months now, just gone half way! She couldn't believe it herself, this was true, she was in a daze, a world of love and happiness where everything was simply peachy. Just before she woke up, a song came to her repeatedly.

'Maiden, Lover, Mother, Crone, Lady of Avalon take me home! Maiden, Lover, Mother, Crone, Lady of Avalon take me home! The Lady, the Lady has answered me, the Lady is calling me home, this is a sign.

I must start preparing!' Brighde was excited, her prayers were answered, they were going home, she just knew it.

Back on the island, Mother Kerr woke up having had an amazing dream of giving birth to Brighde. It was like her actual birth, but something more gentle and loving she felt and all the pain and nervousness around it was gone. It just happened so easily. She knew this was a sign, a message form Brighde, maybe Brighde was coming home soon. This could be it. Normally she wouldn't contact Grandmother Kerridyn but today she knew she had to, it was important. After milking the cows, getting the breakfasts ready and running a few household chores, Mother Kerr hurried all her beloved daughters off with tasks and sent her beloved husband off to work with a delicious lunch.

'You are up to something, my beautiful wife! Aren't you? I just know it, I can see that look in your eyes, I know you too well. I have seen that look before!' he laughed, 'Don't worry I won't tell anyone, I know it's Brighde isn't it? I had a dream of her last night, when she was a baby and I use to take her to see Mother Wolf Mishka and gently help her to connect and feel her protection.'

'Oh darling I cannot keep anything from you, not that I would anyway, yes it is Brighde, I feel she is giving us a message that maybe she is coming home!'

'Let's pray you are right, I will hold her in my heart today.'

'Thank you my love, you really are special. I love you so much.' Both of them kissed lovingly and parted ways. Father Dagda got on his trusted horse. Today Rhiannon was coming with him, for she had chores to do in the village and it was better that they travelled together. Rhiannon leapt up onto her white mare and off they went into the dawn of the new day.

Mother Kerr made her way down the garden path to Grandma Kerridyn's special house, with a gentle knock on the door it opened and there smiling in her magical way was Grandmother Kerridyn.

'Welcome my child, I had a feeling you were coming.'

'Yes, I trust you did, I need your help once more my beloved.'

'Is it to do with Brighde?'

'Yes it is. I had a dream this morning about her coming home, I was giving birth to her again, and it was so easy this time.'

'Can't you see my dearest, Brighde is pregnant with child, she is, Brighde is pregnant!'

'How can this be?' Mother Kerr was amazed and surprised all at once. Tears started running down her cheeks uncontrollably, 'Oh my baby is going to have a baby! Oh my baby!' and Grandmother Kerridyn came and hugged Mother Kerr who was more fragile than normal and helped her to release all her tears and calm her down.

'I have made you a special brew today that is going to help. Now drink this down.'

'Thank you, you are always there for me, I so need this today.'

'I know, I know.'

'Not to worry, all will be well. Brighde will be home soon, just keep lighting candles, the Lady will help, she is returning.'

Mother Kerr smiled and laughed at her silly emotions. Of course everything, was going to be alright, she just knew it. She hugged Grandmother Kerridyn and off she went smiling, getting the house ready, filled with joy and excitement at the prospect of a home coming. There was so much to do. Off she went smiling and singing as she began all the preparations.

The morning had come, Brighde had been preparing for the past few weeks, cooking and cleaning and getting the house in order for Charlie's father so that everything was just right and in harmony. Much had been shared as Charlie's father had naturally guessed that Brighde was pregnant and all the pressure of her hiding it was no longer needed. After several big discussions, everything was decided; Brighde and Charlie would attempt to make it back to the island and if that didn't work, then they would return as best they could and Charlie's father would go out each morning and search the areas around the rivers as best he could in case he saw a sign from Charlie. They had spent the last few months working together every spare moment they had on building another boat that Charlie could have as his own. Charlie was so proud of all the hard work they had put into it together. It was a real achievement on behalf of Charlie and his father and Brighde had cooked endless meals and mended many sore hands with her magic touch to keep them both is high spirits to finish this boat. So the day arrived and Brighde, now over six months pregnant, was really showing.

'You look so beautiful even though now you have this new edition.' Charlie's father was never one for compliments, so this was definitively something special.

'Thank you so much Father for all you have done, you really have been a huge help. You really have been amazing.'

It was an emotional moment for them all as they said their goodbyes and Brighde and Charlie made it into the boat together and sailed off into the rivers that would take them out into the ocean then back into another river then, hopefully they would make it to the sacred lake. Brighde had tears running down her cheeks after saying goodbye. Sailing off she began to chant very sweetly,

'Maiden, Lover, Mother, Crone, Lady of Avalon take us home.' Over and over again softly and quietly so as not to disturb Charlie too much as he was rowing and steering the sails. 'Now where is this special brew I have made to offer the Mother of waters?' She remembered and found the jar of this sacred holy water that she had kept from her beloved home. It was from a fresh spring that she had gathered one day on Grandmother Kerridyn's advice and had slipped the vial in her bra.

With a huge blessing of love she opened it and out it poured into the ocean with all her love and prayers to the Lady of Avalon to take them home. Minutes passed and then there was a breeze that started blowing and within moment became stronger. This was unusual, she thought. As she looked over-head she noticed a flock of swans flying in the air.

'Look at the swans Charlie! That's them, follow them in that direction if you can, that's where they are headed, to the island!'

'Yes my love I can see them, and you may also notice the clouds coming in as well. We are in for some rain I feel if this breeze keeps up, it could be a gail. Hold on my love it's going to get a bit rough!'

'Oh no!' Brighde found the strong rocking quite difficult and was afraid for the baby. She remembered that she had packed her favourite things and had one of her special dolls with her, which she now went to grab. Her name was Penelope. She held Penelope tight and prayed to the Lady that they would arrive home safely, that everything was going to be alright. She wrapped herself up and the waves of water came down, completely saturating them both. 'Oh my gosh this is going to be quite a ride!' She wailed and laughed keeping her spirits high as the waves got bigger and the rain got heavier. She had no idea how long it was going to last. The next thing she knew they were on this huge wave that felt like it was pushing them into the sky. Their wooden boat was flying now as it came down with the speed of lightning, moving out of the ocean to what appeared to be land. 'Could this be possible?' It all happened too quickly for her to know. She closed her eyes, she couldn't handle it, it was all too much.

'Hold On Brighde! We are going down!'

With that their boat catapulted itself high in the sky. Brighde turned slightly but it was moving with such motion that she couldn't see anything at all, until there was a huge bang! They landed on what they thought would be land but turned out to be a huge lake with mists. The boat had been greatly affected by the storm and was shattered in parts. They had lost some of their prized possessions but they were both still alive. Exhausted and cold they held each and fell asleep, it was all too much for them.

Returning Home

Domnu had been out early that morning on the lake, singing and chanting as she did each morning. Nothing had prepared her for what she was to find. She had made her own raft and had a collection of shells that she used to make sounds from. This morning she was guided to do that and when she looked up, she couldn't believe what she saw. There was a raft similar to her's, with what appeared to be two people on it. She hurried and steered her way over to the raft to see what she could do. The mists were rising so it wasn't too difficult. As she was skilled in using her paddle to steer, she managed to get right close up and couldn't believe her eyes, it was Brighde, yet she had changed so much, she was huge, then Domnu realised that she was pregnant! And who was this? She guessed this it was her husband, her partner. Domnu was overjoyed to see her sister, she was ecstatic! She held back her emotions so as not to wake them with her excitement. She had some rope that Father Dagda had told her was always essential to have, wherever she was, thank goodness she had some. With her father's ingenuity she tied the rafts together and carried them back to the shoreline. Once there she sounded her biggest shell, everyone on the island knew that was a special sound and they needed to respond.

Arta was close, as she was weeding in the vegetable patch along with Bambha who was not far away collecting fresh beans. Together they ran until they got to the shoreline, seeing Domnu had brought something in. They were used to their sister now, as she usually collected many unusual things from the shores and would always bring her treasures to lunch for an afternoon of discussion of what it all meant and how it could be used. Some things were practical, like huge pieces of drift wood that later Father

Dagda and her would carry to the workshop. Other times it was a mystery for everyone to work out. This was something else. Arta shouted,

'It's Brighde!' She couldn't help herself. It was loud enough to wake the animals, and to rouse the others from the house. There was huge commotion as everybody came down, Mother Kerr running like the wind,

'My baby has come home!' You would think by now that Brighde and Charlie would awaken, but they had been knocked unconscious by a piece of wood from the boat that had been ripped up by the brute force of the wind and hit both their heads as they blew up into the sky.

Grandmother Kerridyn had also arrived by now and had hot drinks and blankets with her to help them recover.

'Cover them with the blankets first, they must be frozen.' They wrapped them both up, then gently applied heat to their bodies. Stirrings could be heard as Brighde became conscious again.

'Ohhh,' she gasped and burst out with joy, 'I'm home I'm home! I cannot believe it! I thought I was dead! Never to return again. Charlie! Charlie! Is he going to be okay?'

'Give him some time,' Grandma Kerridyn whispered gently. 'It's you we need to get back. Now drink this up!'

Brighde happily drank Grandma Kerridyn's secret brew. Her memories were a daze as she soon collapsed and had to be carried to the house, where she slept for days and sweated, as though she was struggling with fever. Mother Kerr sat by her bed day and night, feeding Brighde her best vegetable soup and more herbs to get her well. One morning Brighde woke up completely looking her normal (pregnant) self and had a huge appetite. Mother Kerr embraced her in her arms.

'Oh my darling girl you are back! Thank goodness, we thought we had almost lost you there for a little while!'

'Yes me too, I don't know what was happened. Where is my Charlie?'

'He has gone out with Father Dagda, he is well and worries about you too. He has happily taken on a new job with Father at his silversmith workshop!'

'That is great news, I was really hoping it would work out for him, I told him how great Father was and how much he could learn.'

'Yes Father Dagda is very happy, he always wanted a son, as he is getting old now, and needs an assistant. Yes that has worked out very well.'

Brighde smiled a huge smile and was so grateful it had worked out. What a journey they had all been on. Thank goodness everyone was okay.

Brighde spent the remaining weeks of her pregnancy very happily with Mother Kerr by her side. They did most things together until Brighde needed her naps and they would reunite again once she woke up.

'I can feel the baby is getting ready to come. I have these cramps now and I can hardly walk, everything is so heavy. Where am I going to give birth?'

Mother Kerr motioned to Brighde to follow her, as she did, she remembered the special tent that she first went into for her menstruation. As Mother Kerr opened the side of the tent, Brighde couldn't believe what she saw. Everything was ready for her to give birth in the tent. They had a warm fire burning, lots of furry skins and what looked like a swinging hammock.

'This my darling is for you. This is your birth position.'

'Wow! Oh this is amazing Mother Kerr, so special.'

'All you do is allow your arms to move over this part of the hammock and then it holds you upright so you can relax your whole upper body into it and just let your body open up and bear down for the baby to come, when you need to push. This will make the final stage easier for you.'

'Thank you so much Mother Kerr, you really are the best. I can't wait for you to be with me through the birth and to meet the baby.'

'I'll be with you all the way. Come and try.'

As Brighde tried it out, she could feel the baby moving down,

'Ohhh it's kicking, oh my gosh, I can feel these cramps, Ooooh!' Then everything calmed down.

'Come my sweet let me massage you, to help everything loosen up.' A special area had been cleared so Brighde could hang over a circular ball as Mother Kerr applied her special pregnancy oil she has blended with herbs of clary sage and rose. It smelt divine. Brighde breathed out all her tension and felt so much more relaxed and calm.

'It's only a matter of days I feel.'

'I think you are right Brighde.' said Mother Kerr.

After the massage Brighde had a nice long nap and relaxed.

The next few nights were quite rough for Brighde as she found herself waking up every hour and a half, peeing and then going back to sleep. She guessed that the baby was already getting her into routine for when it was going to be born. She and Charlie had agreed that they would sleep in different rooms as Charlie was such a light sleeper, Brighde would wake him up with her restlessness. Charlie had been welcomed by her whole family with such love and support it was overwhelming. Her father Dagda was so relieved to have him there, it was like it was meant to be. They both got on really well.

That morning Brighde was up a little earlier than her usual time of 5.30am. She showered and got herself ready to help Mother Kerr with breakfast for both Charlie and Father Dagda and helped them get ready for work. Off they went on horseback and Brighde settled back down to her usual nap. This time she couldn't nap. A huge pain hit her back and she started panting. Could this be it? Earlier that morning she had snuck into Charlie's room and they had made passionate love. Charlie was crazy about her pregnant body and her breasts were so huge now, he couldn't help himself. As she attempted to nap, she kept having a vision of Charlie trying to reach her as though something was up. She didn't want to alert anyone just yet as Mother Kerr had told her that labour could take a long time and that it was best to rest as much as possible and to go for a walk. The pain died down, and Brighde encouraged herself to go for a walk around the island knowing that would ease any contraction she may be having. She kissed Mother Kerr on the cheeks and wished her a lovely morning, she would be back for lunch.

'Stay close to Bambha, she is working in the Fruit Orchard today.'

'Okay, I will do Mother Kerr, thank you.' They both hugged each other as best they could with

Brighde's huge bump pressing in the middle.

'I think you are getting ready.' Mother Kerr said sweetly.

'You just never know.' said Brighde, she didn't want to ring any alarm bells just yet. Off she went.

Just before lunch a messenger came riding on horseback from the village, knocking on Mother Kerr's door. Mother Kerr was surprised, she wasn't used to visitors. It was very rare that someone from the village came to see them, unless it was for an event that they sometimes held. A tall young man brought the news.

'Is it Mother Kerr my lady?'

'Yes it is thank you.'

'There has been a problem at your husband's Silversmith workshop this morning.' Mother Kerr felt great chills moving down her spine.

'Go on,' she whispered.

'Your husband Dagda has been burnt badly in an accident. You must come as soon as possible. My horse will be waiting outside whilst you get yourself ready.'

'Thank you young man. I will get myself ready as soon as possible and have one of my daughters accompany me.'

'As you wish my lady.'

He left the house and waited patiently outside whilst Mother Kerr shouted.

'Rhiannon! Rhiannon! I need you urgently.'

Rhiannon was in the bathroom getting herself ready. She normally never heard Mother Kerr shout, this must be urgent. She pulled on her tunic and raced downstairs to see Mother Kerr in an absolute state.

'What is it Mother? What is going on!'

'Your Father Dagda has been in an accident, he has badly burnt himself, we must go immediately. Get the horses ready at once.'

'Yes Mother Kerr, you must have something to eat.'

'We have no time, we must go immediately! A young gentleman is waiting outside to escort us there.'

'Okay, as you wish.' Rhiannon grabbed a few bananas and scoffed them down as she raced for the horses and saddled them up, getting them ready for their journey. Off they went on horseback galloping at a rapid pace for it was a long two hour journey to reach the village.

As they were galloping through the woods a fox suddenly darted out of nowhere and crossed in front of Mother Kerr's horse. Mother Kerr's horse reared up, frightened by the fox, sending Mother Kerr flying off its back onto a fallen log, breaking her back and knocking her head on a stone. Blood started gushing out of the cut on her head, she was knocked unconscious, losing blood badly. Rhiannon pulled her horse to stop and shouted to the young man ahead to stop. She was screaming hysterically and praying for help! She got down and kneeled beside Mother Kerr holding her hand which was limp in her palm. Mother Kerr was weak and breathing shallow breaths. She looked up and had only a few words left.

'I hand over the house to you and your sisters. You must share everything equally and look after Brighde. I love you so much, so...' with her last breath she died in Rhiannon's arms. Rhiannon was beside herself, screaming and crying hysterically.

'No! Mother Kerr. No! Mother Kerr!'

At the back of the farm Brighde had wandered over very slowly to the fruit tree orchard and her back pain had kicked in again. She stopped and panted with her breath, holding on to a tree for support.

'This really is happening. I am in labour!' she thought, 'Oh my goodness. Bambha! Bambha!'

Bambha was pruning the peach trees and was happily humming to herself, until she swore she could hear her name.

'Bambha! Bambha!'

She had to investigate. She dropped her pruning scissors and followed the sound of the voice. She saw Brighde holding onto to a tree, panting.

'Oh my goodness Brighde is in labour!' She rushed to her side and began rubbing her back, water gushed out through Brighde's legs.

'Ohhh my goodness, my waters have broken, the baby's coming!'

'Just take your time and let's breathe together! In through your nose and out through your mouth, long deep breaths, and now quick short ones panting through your mouth, like you are blowing up a balloon. Phew, phew phew. That's it, let's get you over to the tent.'

The journey to the tent felt like a lifetime, as Brighde had to keep stopping and panting as the contractions intensified each time. They finally made it to the tent. Luckily Mother Kerr has prepared everything the day before. Bambha lit the fire and had Brighde lie over the mound that was covered in animal skins to help her feel supported through her contractions. She was beginning to get hysterical, the pain was taking over. Each time Bambha would hold her and breathe with her bending down onto her knees, keeping her upright, so they were working in harmony with gravity, her pelvis tilted. Nice and easy. A hot pack was now ready for her back and that took the edge off, thank goodness she could feel slightly better now.

The hammock was there ready poised for Brighde to embrace and lie her upper body over it, with her arms supported. She closed her eyes and held onto the ropes to manage the pain, biting into a cow hide that Bambha had prepared for her. Down came Brighde's teeth as another contraction hit, sending waves all over her body. Brighde had visions of Mother Kerr, calling Mother Kerr as her mouth opened again she was shouting Mother Kerr's name without even realising.

'What is it Brighde with Mother Kerr?'

'Mother Kerr,' she cried, 'Mother Kerr, has passed into the other world!'

Bambha thought Brighde was delusional, which can happen in labour. She calmed her down, and gave her herbs to drink, to help her through the motions of the labour. Brighde felt the need to push and gathered all her strength.

'Nice and easy now Brighde! Just trust your body and breath it out, nice deep breaths.'

Brighde focused on her breathing going all the way down and felt a surge of energy through her body and with that surge out came the baby!

'It's a girl!' Bambha screamed with joy, and grabbed the baby as she fell down between Brighde's legs. Brighde dropped down with the pressure and all the fluids were gushing out.

'Just hang in there Brighde, hang in there the baby is still attached. You've got the placenta to still come out. Let me clean the baby down and I'll hand her straight over.'

Brighde grabbed a blanket and covered herself whilst she sat on the end of the mound in the tent and waited for the placenta to come out. She was exhausted and felt all the adrenalin pumping through her body. She began taking more deep breaths to calm herself and all the emotions she was experiencing down. Bambha handed her beautiful baby girl to her, wrapped in a warm soft blanket. Brighde took her baby in her arms and breast fed for the first time. As the colostrum milk came seeping out she felt exhilarated but exhausted at the same time.

'Look at her beautiful mouth and her tiny hands. She is so gorgeous.'

Brighde felt another cramp and shook her body and whoosh, the placenta came rushing out. Brighde felt a burst of energy from the placenta releasing and was again breathing heavily.

'Ohhhh,' she breathed, 'Ohhhh my goodness!'

Bambha, took her time and then quickly cut the cord. By this time Domnu and Arta had arrived to help Brighde, the baby and Bambha to recover. They were filled with joy and take Brighde to have a wash and to get her settled in bed.

That night there was commotion as Rhiannon comes rushing home covered in blood and wild with emotion. She was completely traumatised. Grandmother Kerridyn was in the kitchen ready and waiting for Rhiannon to arrive. One look into each other's eyes and they both knew what had happened.

'Come here my dear, you have done the best you could have. It was destined to happen, you couldn't have done anything else, don't feel bad my child!'

Rhiannon sobbed uncontrollably, and all her tears landed on Grandmother Kerridyn's shoulder. The other sisters came in and Rhiannon shared the news. A huge wave of grief hit everyone and no one could even swallow, they were all completely devastated. It was a night of deep sorrow for everyone. No one told Brighde the news as she was with the baby and needed to be kept stable for her recovery. Bambha agreed and decided to take watch and look after Brighde's recovery, she offered to cook for her and to help her breastfeed. Arta decided to go with Rhiannon to the clinic where Father Dagda was recovering from his burn. They knew that he would be okay but that it would take time. Charlie was with him, recovering from the shock of it all. He was unharmed.

Dark days followed on the farm as Mother Kerr's great light left and transcended into the other world. Each sister prayed every night and lit candles for her soul to cross over in peace. Grandmother Kerridyn led the prayers and sent healing each night for forty days. On the fortieth day Grandmother Kerridyn received a sign that Mother Kerr has crossed over. That morning Grandmother Kerridyn had a dream that she was out in nature and that she was suddenly taken by a beautiful young deer. She was drawn to this deer and followed it into the woods. When she arrived at the place, she saw a horse and heard branches break and then a thud. As she looked, it was Mother Kerr's spirit coming to her.

'I'm with the light now, all will be well. Thank you Mother, look after Brighde, bless you!'

Grandmother Kerridyn felt a great love and warmth in her heart and was then jolted suddenly awake.

The funeral took place weeks later, it was such a difficult day for everyone. Father Dagda was in a state of shock, still wounded from the burns, unable to do anything. Charlie was struggling as well, trying to be there for Brighde, who was finding it difficult to be affectionate again, feeling completely turned off to love after the labour. Everyone was crying and wailing, so upset at Mother Kerr's sudden and dramatic passing. Rhiannon was filled with such strong and dramatic emotions, there was so much she had to work through. To help her come to terms with her trauma Grandmother Kerridyn taught Rhiannon how to journey to the other side. Which she did quite quickly and naturally and without even knowing it, she had helped Mother Kerr cross over to the light. After that she found peace and received the Dove as a gift from spirit. Her red hair now showed a strip of white. This was a symbol of her wisdom coming through.

The baby kept everyone going, as the days flew by, no one really knew what day it was. Only that the baby was growing and that Brighde was in a dangerous place. She was an emotional roller-coaster, some days she was happy and smiling, other days she was filled with tears and depressed. She was struggling to come to terms with losing Mother Kerr, being strong for her little one and learning how to be a good partner to Charlie as well. She named the little one 'Brigit-Ana'. Grandmother Kerridyn held a blessing for Baby Brigit-Ana one night to help Brighde find strength. All the sisters came together to represent the elements. She received a blessing of Earth from Bambha and a blessing of Air from Great Aunt Danu who suddenly appeared for Mother Kerr's funeral having been gone for a long time, she decided to stay and help the family. The blessing of Fire came from Arta and the Water blessing came from Domnu. It was a small ceremony held in the kitchen over the hot stove fire. Father Dagda and Charlie both had little gifts for Brigit-Ana, which they had made and that cheered Brighde up immensely. They could see she was getting better and had patience for her and her recovery. Charlie knew how much Mother Kerr meant to her, he wasn't expecting things to be all rosy overnight. He had a good heart and knew that Brighde needed time. Baby Brigit-Ana was blessed with love and all the positive gifts that life could bring. She was a happy baby but also sensitive to her mother's emotions so she would cry a lot and that was hard for Brighde to handle. Grandmother Kerridyn could see she was in trouble.

'Why don't you go outside Brighde and have some fresh air and sun? I'll look after Baby Brigit-Ana.' Brighde was grateful and wandered outside.

It was this time in the afternoon that there would be moments of sunshine when the sun was shining and all Brighde could do was to lie down on the grass and feel the warmth of the sun shining on her body. It was at this time that she was reminded of how grateful she was to be alive. She remembered what it felt like to be alive and enjoy life again. Something she never thought was possible after losing Mother Kerr so suddenly. She felt she needed to punish herself, that somehow it was her fault, even though it wasn't. She struggled with her guilt. Then once again as she lay down, she embraced the sunshine and allowed the warmth and the heat of the sun to melt away all her pain. Sun in the sky, sun on her back, all she could do was be happy that she was alive; this was a great gift from the sun. She also had the gift of her daughter Brigit-Ana. She needed to be strong for Brigit-Ana, to show her that her mother could cope.

Finding the path that she used to walk as a child again, she found her self singing once again and feeling drawn to go to her cave, if only she could remember the way. She hadn't been there for such a long time, not since the first time she had accidentally left the island. She remembered turning and seeing the path with all the trees overgrown now. She bent down and saw the opening still there and struggled to get inside. She looked around and saw some of her dolls still there, now covered in dirt. Some of her favourite crystals and some candles are still there too. Brighde sat down and bursts into tears, crying for Mother Kerr. She began praying to the Lady to help her overcome her grief at losing Mother Kerr, her beloved Mother Kerr whom she loved so much and was so looking forward to sharing her baby with her. She sobbed so much until she hadn't got any tears left, and she fell into silence. She remembered how to meditate when she prayed and this time she was calmer. Suddenly she saw Mother Kerr before her, looking radiant and alive reaching out to give her a warm hug.

'You must leave the island Brighde my love,' she said, 'You must go with Charlie and baby Brigit-Ana into the water and trust where the waters will guide you. The Lady will be with you.'

'How did she know about the Lady?' Brighde wondered, 'she must be with the Lady now.'

As if Mother Kerr had read her thoughts, she said, 'Yes I am with the Lady and she will take you to a new place. When the time is right, not yet my love. Meanwhile you must spend time and learn the sight and the ways of Grandmother Kerridyn.'

Brighde nodded and was just about to thank Mother Kerr with a huge hug but she was gone, leaving a warm feeling in Brighde's heart. She felt slightly better and was so grateful to Mother Kerr for giving her this vision. It was like a huge cloud had lifted off her. She made her way back home and felt a lot better. She shared her vision with Grandmother Kerridyn who understood that Brighde was now ready for her training.

Everything was arranged in the household so that Brighde was allowed to spend many hours with Grandmother Kerridyn whilst Arta, Domnu, Rhiannon and Bambha looked after the household duties; keeping the farm alive and taking it in turn to look after Baby Brigit-Ana. Baby Brigit-Ana was loved and nurtured by all of her aunts and Charlie and Father Dagda would take it in turns to read her bedtime stories every night, even if she was too small to understand.

Leaving the Island

Soon the day came and as hard as it was, Brighde said her goodbyes. She loved her sisters so much and her Father Dagda, who had aged dramatically since losing Mother Kerr. Father Dagda had given her such great gifts and had helped Charlie so much to develop himself and his skills as a blacksmith. Off they went again, this time in a new boat that Charlie and Father Dagda had made with the help of Domnu. It was a sad and cheery farewell as they wished them both off and it was very hard for the sisters to say goodbye to Baby Brigit-Ana, who they had all bonded with so strongly. Brighde made offerings to the sea and prayed to the Lady that they would be guided to go where she was meant. As soon as she finished her prayers the mists came down and they were shrouded in darkness. Charlie kept rowing despite the fact he couldn't see anything. The boat was moving and Brighde and baby Brigit-Ana had fallen asleep. When they awoke, they were surrounded by water. Dark clouds came, there was rumbling and the boat started to rock. Charlie shouted to Brighde, 'Hold on! It's going to be a rough ride.' The storm broke and there was great thunder and lightning as the boat moved high up onto the waves. Brighde was holding onto Baby Brigit-Ana for her dear life. Charlie was steering the boat as best he can.

The waves were getting higher and stronger by the minute. Another spark of lightning came striking down and the boat split into two. Charlie was pushed forward by the impact and Brighde screamed as she held onto Baby Brigit-Ana and prayed for their lives. Brighde suddenly had a vision of the Mother Wolf Mishka that had helped bring her up. She remembered how it would howl at night every time she would go to sleep. Deep deep down in her spirit she called to Mishka, Mother Wolf, to come and show her the way and to look after Baby Brigit-Ana and Charlie her beloved. She closed her eyes and held Baby Brigit-Ana tight then felt this huge push like she was being lifted up high into the sky. Suddenly she experienced a massive drop and felt her stomach in her mouth as down they went together. She screamed for her life. As they plunged down into the water Brighde was struggling, fighting for her life, pushing baby Brigit-Ana up first to make sure she had air to breathe. Brighde then found her feet, out they came from the water and she crashed onto the shoreline with her baby in her arms. She was completely exhausted and delirious and that was where she stayed.

The Tribe of 'Tuatha de Danann'

Shouting was heard as young girls who had been collecting seaweed on the beach had raised the alarm.

'Alive!' they shouted. 'Woman and child! Alive!'

The young girls had long red hair and markings on their forehead with deep green eyes. They caressed Brighde's hair, which was something her Mother Kerr used to do to her as a child. Brighde loved it. It woke her up straight away and she began screaming.

'Brigit-Ana, where is my baby, Brigit-Ana?!'

As she turned her head, she saw Brigit-Ana crawling on all fours smiling and playing with these beautiful young girls. She sighed a huge sigh of relief. Then all the memories of the boat breaking and Charlie being pushed into the waves in front of her came flooding back.

'Where is my husband Charlie? Charlie!' Brighde shouted, 'Charlie!' Brighde managed to scramble to her feet, she was still in a state of shock and dehydration. She was hysterical. 'Where is Charlie?'

She paced up and down the beach, searching, looking, shouting for Charlie! Charlie! Charlie! She couldn't see him anywhere. She was becoming more and more upset and panicking. She ran back to the little girls who were playing with her baby Brigit-Ana and she collapsed and passed out. As she hit the ground her head landed on a rock, Brighde was out like a light with a huge thump.

When she woke up, she was no longer on the shoreline, and all she could feel was her head throbbing, heavy and pounding. A young woman stood up and came over to her side.

'Oh you have woken up. You have been gone for hours. We were quite concerned about you! Here drink this tea, it will help sooth your throbbing head.'

'Thank you' Brighde whispered, she could hardly speak.

'It's our pleasure and warmest welcome to you and your baby. Don't worry your baby is absolutely fine. She is being fed and washed, and she will be with you shortly. We have been anticipating your arrival. Our mother was gifted with a vision that you would arrive with your baby and bring many gifts and blessings to our land. You will be initiated into our tribe and culture!'

'Where am I?' Brighde asked.

'You are in Ireland, you have come home. We are the Tribe of Tuatha de Danann.'

Initiation of the Fiery Arrows

The next morning Brighde woke up to a great commotion. There had been much talk going on and preparations had been made for Brighde to be initiated into the Tribe. The eldest member introduced herself as Mother Amelia.

'We had a vision that you would come with a small child and that you and your child would make the final magic number of nineteen. We have prepared a great fire ceremony for you, to meet your higher self and take the gift that life is giving you. It has been fore-told that you will become a Seer, a great healer, that you will heal many and your name will be known by hundreds of people across this land. Time will pass and your spirit will rise into the light. For you are Brighde, Bride, Lady of the Gail. You are the one my Lady!'

Brighde was taken aback, but in a daze, still grieving the loss of her beloved Charlie. She nodded, all she could do was surrender. She was led into a tent, where she was washed down and dressed in what appeared to be a leather skirt and bustier top that fitted her perfectly. She was given leather bands that were tied onto both wrists. A crown was placed on her glowing red hair. She was painted with sacred markings, which were preparations for later on where she would be marked permanently, a mark of initiation. A bow and arrow were placed before her.

'This is your gift from the tribe. We all have one. This is what you will be firing tonight.'

Brighde took the bow and arrow and somehow it shook her out of her reverie and brought her into a place of strength.

She felt great fires burning in her belly, mixed emotions of pain, of suffering, of loss and anger. She was ready to begin! As she walked out of the tent, she saw a huge fire burning in the centre of their gathering. She saw a circle of seventeen women, all dressed the same as her with their own unique markings. All of them carried a bow and arrow, they were ready, poised for action. The sound of a horn blared out into the sky and drums started to beat. The women began chanting, repeating an intoxicating rhythmic chant. The fire in the centre of their circle was lit and all the women came together, chanting out loud, surrounding Brighde. She found herself next to the fire, in the centre of the circle and she began to unleash all her pain, her anger, her disbelief at what had happened. She started dancing wildly around the circle taking huge leaps as she expressed deep inner wounds, pain inside. The intensity of the women's chanting increased. She felt herself go deeper and deeper and could feel a great heat rising up inside of her. This heat was awakening her, and she moved with the heat in her body, letting it take her over. She completely surrendered. Everything that had upset her seemed to ease as this great fire took over her completely.

As she connected deep inside, she could feel the healing energy of peace, love and acceptance grow in her heart. Just as she found this place inside the drumming stopped. The women stepped back and formed a circle around her. One by one they came up to her and bowed before herand each gave her a blessing. Then each one lit their arrow from the centre of the fire and released it high in the sky flaming brightly. It moved in the direction of the ocean, anachronistically one by one as each woman fired one after each other. Brighde could see a huge wave of flaming arrows moving towards the ocean. As the last one was lit and flying high the woman turned and looked Brighde right into her eyes signalling it was her turn. As Brighde stood, still preparing herself mentally for what she was about to do, the leader of the tribe came up to her and asked her to open the palms of her hands. She placed her hands ontop of Brighde's and a tremendous energy passed between them. Brighde was overtaken by this incredible feeling.

'I am one of you, I have returned to join you. You have given me this great gift of healing. I am speechless how can I thank you?'

'You don't have to say anything my child, for we already know who you are.'

With that Brighde turned and her baby Brigit-Ana, looking like a little girl, was brought beside her all dressed up in an amazing tribal dress with the same markings painted on her skin. Her hair was tied in the traditional way.

'You must hand your bow and arrow to your daughter to touch, and that will initiate her into the tribe.'

'Ok I will give it to her, then she will give it back to me.'

'Yes, that's right.'

Then it happened, this great exchange took place between mother and child. When Brighde handed her bow and arrow to Brigit-Ana she was amazed at how well she handled it with such grace. Brighde could see that her daughter Brigit-Ana had a special gift that she hadn't recognised before glowing inside of her. When Brighde took the bow and arrow back, she couldn't believe how much the energy of the arrow and bow had changed. There was so much love and power, it blew Brighde away. She held it tight, thanking her beloved daughter.

'Now you must light the arrow.' beckoned Mother Amelia.

Brighde lit the arrow and as she did she felt this incredible power rising through her. She placed the arrow in the slow, pulling the strong of the bow back ready to release it into the sky. As she let it go, a swan came out of nowhere and flew right next to the arrow guiding it to the sea. Brighde felt tears trickle down her cheek, she knew Mother Kerr was there, maybe she was the swan! Far far away, out into the ocean, her arrow flew. The whole tribe began chanting again surrounding Brighde and Brigit-Ana.

They lifted them both up onto their hands as they formed a platform for them to lie on. They carried them both around the fire three times, anointing them with their love. Then they gently dropped them down onto the ground, letting them both onto their feet. The fire began to ease and one by one the woman of the tribe walked across the fire, strong willed and full of intention. They were hearing the call of their spirit. They wove a beautiful pattern into the ashes as each one crossed the fire untouched by the ashes. Now it was Brighde's turn. She took the lead and with all her might and strength she walked across the fire, surprised and relieved not to feel anything. She had passed the initiation. She was now part of the Tribe of the Tuatha de Danann.

By the end of the evening Brighde felt relieved and in a daze, feeling completely out of it. Before she knew it, she was guided out of the ceremony and into a warm cosy tent with lots of animal furs, pillows and warm blankets. There was her daughter Brigit-Ana who had already fallen asleep. Without any hesitation Brighde thanked her guide and dropped down onto the soft woolly blankets and was instantly fast asleep.

The Legend of Brighde

From that moment on Brighde became a very powerful healer and Seer. Her reputation spread all over Ireland and many people came from far and wide to be able to experience her healing and see her in person. They brought their wounded family members, their sick children and animals. Brighde received much love and support from the Tribe of the Tuatha de Danam. They taught her how to use her gifts and how to heal with herbs and natural medicines. All the training she had done with grandmother Kerridyn had been really helpful, for what she was learning was very similar and her teachers were amazed at how quickly she picked everything up.

Brighde spent her time with the people of Ireland. Her daughter also grew up with these great skills as she learned at the same time that Brighde did. There was much love and joy shared among the women of the tribe. With time Brighde came to realise why her Mother Kerr had mentioned to her when she was a child that one day she would grow up and be something special and be able to help people in a loving way. She always remembered Mother Kerr's ways and held her deep in her heart, never forgetting the beautiful love they shared together. She also remembered the gift of having Charlie, a wonderful man who showed her love and what that meant. Every night before she went to sleep Brighde would send love to her mother and thank her in her prayers, as well as Charlie, Father Dagda, Grandmother Kerridyn and all her beautiful sisters whom she shared her childhood with. One day, she thought, one day they would all be reunited together again.

Many years passed and much changed among the Irish people. Christianity had come although still allowing the Celtic tribes to stay. This time it was different and Protestant Churches were being built and a new religion was enforced, leading people away from the tribe. There were many discussions between Brighde and the Tuatha de Danann on the future of their safety. Everyone knew it was time to gather together and make a decision. It was time to leave before things took a turn for the worse. Everyone gathered their belongings together and parted ways. Brighde was getting old and her daughter Brigit-Ana was now a stunning young woman with a new life in front of her. So they left their loving home and parted ways with their tribe of sisters, uniting once more before they all left with their fiery arrows. After this everyone dispersed and the Legend that was Brighde went underground for many years. During this time many people were killed and homes were destroyed if you did not follow the way of the the Church. Brigit-Ana was guided by Brighde to go far far away and settle in a small village called Kildare.

They settled in Kildare and Brighde began writing poetry and would perform it with Brigit-Ana in the local village square. Brigit-Ana painted a silver birch branch in silver and added tiny bells on it. When Brighde would read the words of her poems, she would shake the silver bells and her audience would know that she had reached the end of one poem and that soon she would be starting a new one. The word spread and people began to gather in the village. They were intrigued by the incredible words and sometimes songs that would come out of Brighde's mouth. She would describe far away places that sounded like paradise, where there was an abundance of fruit and vegetables. There was love of sisterhood, of mother and father. Brighde would play on the words and have Brigit-Ana dress up in animal outfits imitating swans, sometimes wolves, sometimes snakes, and even cows. People became mesmerised and would bring them cooked food and bread, offering it to them as a thank you. Brighde was grateful for their support as money was scarce. They would also bring their children who just loved listening to the stories that Brighde would tell. The children would laugh and shout when Brigit-Ana would growl or moo to imitate the animals. Everyone had great fun together. Brighde's poetry and song evenings became a regular occurrence in the village. With that Brighde's reputation grew again and more people would come and make donations, it was enough for them to live on.

One evening, while Brighde was reciting Grandma Kerridyn's favourite recipes, which she had remembered from being with her, she felt her back creak and she keeled over, unable to move at all. Brigit-Ana was by her side instantly.

'Mother, Mother are you ok?'

'I'm not my child, I must take rest, I can hardly move. Please help me get back home to bed.'

Brigit-Ana called over to some men to help carry her mother Brighde to their humble home so she could have some rest. From that day on Brighde became bed ridden.

Brigit-Ana had acquired an admirer from their poetry nights and the pair had fallen in love and had been seeing each other for a while now. Brighde noticed the same look that she once had when she had fallen in love with Charlie. She prayed that all would be well for the two of them and that they would be able to be together. Time passed quickly and before Brighde knew it, she could hear the sound of little feet and baby Meeka was born. Brighde had to be moved to a nursing home run by nuns. She didn't know what day it was or how much time had passed, she had entered another world. Having both Brighde at home as well as the baby was too much for Brigit-Ana to manage. Brighde was aware of it and accepted her fate, that it had to be this way. Her body was no longer capable of functioning on its own. She needed someone to help her to wash, go to the toilet and feed her. Brighde was becoming more and more distant and her voice changed. She use to have such a lovely loud voice, which she would use with great skill and grace to attract people's attention. She knew how to use it well to recite poetry and how to be gentle when she would heal people and speak to them giving words of advice. Now her voice was very faint, she could barely whisper some days. There wasn't much she was able to do physically with movement. Her legs had gone and she was only just able to move her arms.

Most days she would attempt to read a little, then she would drift off to sleep, where she would faze in and out of consciousness. Whenever Brigit-Ana came to visit her mother and hold her hand, Brighde would talk of the cave. She called it a special cave, where there were little dolls that she had made. It was here that she could see the Lady calling her, saying come home, you are coming home. Sometimes she would be conscious, sometimes she wouldn't be. It was very hard for Brigit-Ana to watch her mother slowly deteriorate in front of her. Brigit-Ana knew now it was only a matter of time. Her daughter Meeka was growing up now and loved coming to visit Grandma Brighde in the nursing home. She would bring her little animals she had made and paintings that she had done at home. Meeka's work covered the walls of her room and that really lifted Brighde's heart to see her granddaughter doing so well. She knew that some day soon the Lady would take her home and she also knew that little Meeka would also have a special calling.

One morning Brigit-Ana was getting ready to see her mother Brighde and was calling Meeka to prepare herself for going out. She didn't get a response out of Meeka.

'Why was she doing that? That naughty child,' she thought. 'Meeka, Meeka its time to go now! Shall I come and get you!' The big bad mummy wolf is coming to get you!'

She knew Meeka loved this game as she had a love of wolves just like Grandma Brighde. She had no idea how she could feel so connected to wolves not ever having had met one.

'I'm in the cave Mummy!' Meeka sang.

'Cave?' thought Brigit-Ana, 'What cave is she talking about?'

She went to her daughters room to find out. To her surprise Meeka has taken all the sheets off her bed and had transformed her bedroom into this giant cave, placing a few of her dolls and animals in the centre, with her biggest fluffiest blanket on the floor.

'What on earth are you doing Meeka? Oh my goodness how are you going to sleep now?'

'I'm hoping to see Grandmother Brighde in her cave!' squeaked Meeka.

'No Meeka we are going to see Grandma Brighde in her special home.'

'No Mummy, Grandma Brighde is in her cave, I know she is, she came to visit me this morning and told me so!'

'Really my darling Meeka? That is unbelievable, but anything is possible with Grandma Brighde!'

The phone rang, and Brigit-Ana left Meeka and ran to get it. It was the nursing home. They told Brigit-Ana that Brighde had passed away this morning peacefully in her sleep. She said all the nuns were there praying for her, she was with God now. Tears flooded down Brigit Ana's face. She thanked the nuns for their kindness and dropped the phone back down. She came back into Meeka's bedroom and gave her a huge hug.

'Yes you were right my darling angel. Grandma Brighde has gone into her cave now and crossed over. She is with her Mother Kerr now. Bless you my child, you really are special.'

She gave Meeka another big hug and together they spent the rest of the morning lying down together in Meeka's cave. Brigit-Ana's heart melted knowing what was to come. Her mother was at peace now. She thought that was the best she could have hoped for, for her mother.

Chapter 3

Brighde's Mythical Animals

Swan
Image courtesy of Steve Dixson

Rising Phoenix
Aquarell on watercolor paper
Isabella Weber

This chapter is a series of mediations that came to me whilst calling the Goddess Brighde into my life. I invite you to journey with me and connect with her animals.

Journey to Meet The Phoenix

Sit down comfortably with your legs crossed ready for meditation, or in a chair, or lying down on your back. Just allow yourself to breathe deeply in through your nose and out through your mouth. Now become aware of any tension in your body and with your breath feel this tension, fee all the stress moving down out of body and through the floor and into the earth below you.

Now become aware of your heart. Feel your heart beating and take 3 deep slow breaths into your heart. Feel your heart opening up, see it like a flower reaching it's petals out to the sun taking in it's first breath. Breathe into your heart. Imagine your heart beating like the heart of Mother Earth, that you are connected from below, that the centre of the earth is beating at the same rhythm as your heart is beating together as one. As you breath you imagine your thoughts are like clouds in the sky, passing by. You begin to feel more relax and are starting to let go now of a second wave of tension as Mother Earth again draws it all out of your body like a magnet, leaving you feeling heavy and relieved. Feeling all the tension leaving your body as you breath in the breath of life, and begin to notice the vibrant healing energy that surrounds you. You imagine a Giant violet flame of energy is rising from the centre of Mother Earth all the way up through the floor into your body, completely surrounding you in the violet flame. Allow the violet flame to cleanse and purify all the negative thoughts that are still hanging around, any remaining stress or tension. Notice all the demands that are placed on you on a daily basis, the commitments that you have. See these completely releasing like great bars of steel, feel like you can completely let go and allow yourself to be fully present in the moment. As you breathe the flame moves through you and all your tension, all your stress is released with the out breath out of your body and back into the earth as the violet flames returns to the centre of mother earth.

Imagine yourself entering a beautiful tropical paradise. The sun is shining and you can feel the warmth melting away all your tension, aches and pains in your body and you become absorbed by the lush tropical vegetation that surrounds you. You notice the coconut palm trees and the huge green luscious banana leaves that brush pass you. You can hear the rushing sound of running water, that gently washes away memories of the past fears and worries that have kept coming back to haunt you. There is a path in front of you and you follow it as it leads you down into the lush green vegetation and beautiful exotic red flowers. There are brightly coloured butterflies that fly straight past you and you can see in the distance a huge mountain. Somehow your instinct tells you this is where you are headed.

As you walk you feel a gentle breeze on your cheeks and you feel the wind blow through your hair. All your worries are being blown away as you become in awe of your incredible exotic surroundings. The climb to the mountain begins and as you look around you, you notice huge black rocks that have been moulded into strange shapes. You are intrigued and you run your hands over the rock, you realise that this rock was once liquid lava that had spilled out from the volcano. You are climbing a volcano! Your heart begins to pound, and a sense of fear washed over you, then quickly passes as your desire to climb to the top strengthens.

The walk becomes quite difficult, you are using a lot of effort and energy as you push your way up the steep rocky slopes, slipping on the broken black gravel rocks as you climb foot by foot all the way up. You climb over fallen trees, and duck quickly to avoid big tree branches that are there in front of you. Then the shrub starts to clear and you notice a huge crater at the top of the volcano that is emitting a steamy heat that rises up from the centre of the earth. You have reached the top! You notice a small crack in the earth, you bend down and run your hand over it, surprised at how much heat is rising out of it. It really is alive. You take 3 deep breaths and feel great sense of achievement and elation as you have climbed this huge volcano. As your breath starts to quieten you start to feel cold as you so high above the clouds. You know you need to keep moving. Suddenly you hear a sound and your instinct tells you to follow it. You notice a pathway that leads down into the volcano and you follow it with great anticipation. You begin the down ward climb down steep steps and you begin to smell the smoke of a fire burning. One more set of steps and you turn and see an entrance to a cave. You follow the smoke and you are guided to bend down and crawl through a narrow opening. Now you have entered the Cave of the Phoenix. Sitting down to rest, you are transfixed by a huge fire that is burning in front of you. As you stare into the flames, you begin to make the outline of an incredibly stunning bird. It is a 'Phoenix!' You have always dreamed of meeting the phoenix face to face to experience its gift of transformation. You hear a voice that is talking inside your head, you can't believe that the phoenix has been waiting to meet you.

'Welcome to my home, you have journeyed well. I am here to help you to heal the deep karmic wounds inside your heart, that connects you to your soul! Look into the flames, do not be afraid of burning yourself, you are completely safe. Allow the flames to touch you deeply and be open to what they show you. You may go into a trance state and remember times of pain and sorrow. Difficulties that have occurred in your life may surface. This may be times of hardship, loss of those you love, accidents, arguments. What ever you see in the flames, allow the heat of the fire to cleanse and release your inner pain by breathing it out of your body. Let the heat become a catalyst for drawing out all that is painful, that you don't wish to feel any more. Let your wounds be healed, let the pain go, you don't have to feel like this any more.'

You thank the Phoenix and stare into the flames, and images of your life begin to flash before you. Memories surface from when you were a young child. Difficult events, trauma's, times of crisis when you felt you couldn't cope and were all alone. The same feelings you felt back them return with a vengeance and you are overwhelmed with emotion as you revisit the pain when it first happened. You remember what the Phoenix said and you breathe and blow it out through your mouth into the flames and allow the warmth of the fires to sooth your soul. Now the pain has disappeared just as quickly as it had never been there before. The flames have swallowed it up and have replaced it with a great sense of warmth, resolution and acceptance. Stay here for as long as you need to, to allow yourself to be purged of all your wounds. Then when you feel clear and content look at me The Phoenix. Watch my wings change colour. Watch my body change shape as I rise from the ashes, whole again, renewed, stronger than before! You watch the Phoenix merge into a flurry of different colours that flicker and capture your entire vision. You feel your emotional, mental, physical and spiritual self becoming aligned, you feel whole again.

Take 3 more deep breaths feeling your body as one. Bring your awareness to your hand and feet and notice your consciousness coming back to this reality. Have a good stretch and feel grounded back from the other world. Imagine a colour from the Phoenix and see yourself wrapped up in it, like a blanket closing you in safely, from the top of your head all the way down to your feet. Feel the ground beneath you and take your time. When you feel ready stand up and drink a glass of water to ground your self.

Maiden Snake
Aquarell on watercolor paper
Isabella Weber

Working With The Snake Maiden

Make yourself comfortable with either your legs crossed in lotus position, or one leg crossed in front of the other. You may also find that you can sit comfortably with your back straight on a chair. Have your palms facing upwards and take this time to begin to focus on your breathing. |Take a deep breaths in, all the way down to your abdomen, then take a deep breath out through your mouth.

Bring your awareness to your third eye, and as you focus on your third eye, imagine an eye in front of you opening. Bring your awareness to your base chakra, which is located at the base of your spine. This is the home of your kundalini, your sacred divine sexual energy. Imagine your base chakra like a cave with a red fire burning in the centre. Call to Mother earth and ask Brighde, Brigantia ancient earth mother to activate your divine kundalini energy. As you breath and give this intention, imagine a snake in any shape of form coming into your awareness, appearing in your cave. Do not be afraid, allow any fears or phobias to be absorbed into the red fires of your base chakra. Now begin to make a sound, of So Hum. 'So Hum' is a yogic mantra that is a reflection of the sound of the breath and also carries a more profound meaning of: 'I am that' So means 'I am' and Hum means 'That'. This connects with you all of creation the one breathing us all. As you sound and repeat this mantra allow yourself to completely surrender to the sound chanting as loud as you can. As you sound and repeat this mantra So Hum, your snake begins to rise from the base of your spine and begins to travel up, all the way up to your third eye. Just take your time and allow this to happen naturally. With each repetition of the sound Sooooo imagine the snake rising up to your third eye. Then with each repetition of the sound Hummmmmm imagine it travelling all the way down back to your base chakra.

Just simply take your time to familiarise and practice this meditation, and as you do, you may begin to feel that your body wants to start shaking. If it does start shaking this is a sign that your Mother Shakti; (this is your divine creative feminine power described in Hinduism as The Great Divine Mother). It is the cosmic energy of creation. This process can activate and awaken your Mother Shakti life force energy and it may begin moving up your spine through your chakras, cleansing and releasing all that is ready to be cleared. The Mother Shakti life force energy moves in it's own way, so just trust and surrender to what is happening to your body and move with it.

After experiencing this practice, settle down again making your self comfortable and bring your awareness to your third eye and chant OM 3 times. This raises your vibration and opens up your consciousness, enabling you to connect with your higher self.

Imagine yourself in the desert. The heat of the sun is pouring down on you and sweat is beginning to drip off your face, your neck and shoulders. You are thirsty and dying for a drink of water. Every step you take feels like you are drawing on a huge amount of energy just to move forward. You feel yourself becoming exhausted. You look in front of you and see the horizon and there appears to be some palm trees. Is this a mirage you ask yourself? Are you day dreaming or is this real? You keep moving, and don't know how it is possible, It is as though something is drawing you to the Palm trees, and you pray it is a water hole. You can feel yourself really getting tired now, and if you don't rest soon, you feel as though you are going to pass out completely. The heat of the sun is shining down on your back. Your head is wrapped in a turban and you look above into the sky and see a huge bird with great wings circling above you. This must be a sign that there is life not too far ahead. You struggle and keep pushing ahead until you are almost on your hands and knees. Then you drop down onto the ground suddenly with no energy left.

As you collapse in a heap you suddenly hear a rattle sound and a ssshhhhhhhhhhh. You recognise this sound as a slow moving snake. You turn your head and see a huge cobra poised head high, ready to strike. You stay still and watch the cobra move down like a lightning bolt in front of you. You watch and notice that it is going for a scorpion in front of you that you failed to notice. In a second the cobra has swallowed the scorpion into its' mouth and you can see it moving down its' slithery body.

You look into its' eyes and it reflects back to you your greatest fear that you have always struggled with and yet felt incapable of doing anything about. No matter how many times it would catch you unawares, and upset you and the people you love the most. You felt exposed, vulnerable, incapable of change, completely paralysed. The snake turns and darts away with its' prey in its' stomach now. You have been released, Saved! Still alive! You can not believe what has just happened.

You feel your whole body shaking and your worst fears are surfacing. All that has been sitting beneath the surface in your deep unconscious is shedding like a snake's skin. You are ready to release this fear that holds you back from fully loving yourself. You shudder and shake your whole body. You let go and enter a deep state of conscious awareness. Memories from childhood and from the past surface and then disappear again. You feel really cold, like something has happened. You body is calling you back. You become aware of your legs, you stretch them out in front of you and release them, You let go of any more tension in your body and find a warm blanket to wrap yourself up in. Make yourself a hot drink and relax.

Invocation to the Great Cosmic Cow Mother

This next invocation shows you how to connect to the Divine Cow Mother. This is working with the Mother aspect of Brighde, and is intended to help you to relate and find your own maternal energy. The Cow Mother is also known as Hathor, who is an Egyptian Deity of music, pleasure, and dance. She helps to open people up to receiving.

Think about your own relationship with your mother. How was she as a person. Take time to write down a description for yourself to help you identify your own Mother patterns that you may have adopted or rejected from your Mother.

Take time now to look into your own tenancies and patterns. Do you find it easy to receive? Are you a giver naturally or do you find yourself constantly taking from life and never feeling fulfilled? Asking yourself these questions will help you identify with your Mother patterns. To help you start the process you can invoke the Cow Mother to help you to connect and heal them.

To begin your journey with the Cow Mother plan a trip where you can go to local farm where they milk cows and possibly produce yoghurt, milk or cheeses. See this trip as a sacred journey with the intention of meeting the Cow Mother. Also it is good to reflect on your diet. Are you allergic to dairy products, it's not necessary to eat or drink them, simply to appreciate the nourishment that they bring. You can work visually instead of eating them. Ask yourself; do you eat cheese and diary products? Do you like ice cream, and anything creamy? Do you drink milk, how does that make you feel? Have you had a baby and breastfeed, what did that experience bring up for you? What makes you feel fulfilled? Do you eat beef? In India cows are considered sacred and represent the divine. You may wish to change your diet and become vegetarian.

When you go to the farm, spend time learning about the cows, and if possible have a go at milking them yourself, and see how you respond. Is it enjoyable? Does it bring you pleasure? Are you able to connect with your own approach to Mothering and what that means to you?

After your farm experience. Come back home and create an alter dedicated to the Cow Mother. Find pictures of cows that you like. Choose coloured candles to light and place on your alter. Also see this alter dedicated to your Divine Mother and the Mother that you wish to be yourself. Sit with yourself and ask your truth, find your gentle caring side, does that come easily to you? Or do you feel deprived and in need of more Mother Love, nurturing and care. Find an image of your Mother or a Mother Figure in your life that you love and place this on your alter. Gather your photos together with your candles and offer a glass of milk on your alter as well to symbolise receiving. This milk represents the divine love and nurturing of the Cosmic Cow Mother who fills you up with her endless abundance of love and ask her

Brighde's Cow with the Red Ears
Aquarell on watercolor paper
Isabella Weber

in prayer to help you to be more open to receiving. Here is a prayer that you can adapt for your self and your personal needs:

Invocation to the Great Cosmic Cow Mother

'Divine Mother, great Mother of us all, I call to you, Brighde Cow Mother of abundance, of the bounty of milk and all it's pleasures. Come Cow Mother I call to you to come and be here now with me and share your nurturing presence. With your blessings and love help me to be open to receiving more love and fulfilment in my life. Come and be with me and ground me into this world in my physical body. Help me to find real wisdom and goodwill unto others. Help me to forgive my own Mother and heal my ancestral Mother patterns so I can learn from her. Help me to be grateful and positive for my life and all that I have.'

Now imagine yourself going into a huge luscious green meadow, where the sun is shining and you can see butterflies. A gentle breeze blows through your hair and you can feel it on your cheeks. You walk along the lovely lush grass and see a herd of cows nearby. You lie on the soft green grass and take some nice deep breaths and relax. Hand all your stress over to the Great Mother Earth, by imaging it releasing down through the earth, letting go in your heart. As you relax you imagine a beautiful imagine of your Mother or a Divine Mother figure and she is pouring all this unconditional love into your heart. You are so happy to receive this and feel full of love, fulfilled and whole. You hear the cows around you, munching on the grass, happy content, not wanting for anything more.

Bring your awareness to everything that has happened between you and your Mother. Begin to release all these feelings through your breath, and imagine they are moving towards the Cow Mother who is happily eating it up, just like the soft green grass. She is lapping up all your pain, your suffering, misunderstanding, all that has been difficult. She is taking on your Ancestral Mother patterns, this is all that you have struggled with, not being able to receive, feeling stuck, unloved and rejected. This Divine Mother Cow has a huge appetite for all that hasn't worked out in your life between you and your Mother. She continues to swallow and absorb all that you are releasing, taking it on like there is no tomorrow. You feel a huge sense of relief that this Divine Mother Cow is capable of taking this all on and transforming it, into her body.

You are feeling now a great sense of relief that this beautiful Mother Cow is taking all this on for you, you thank her from the bottom of your heart. In your heart you now feel a wonderful, joyful feeling that is beginning to blossom. You are seeing the sun shining, and are so happy to have received the Divine blessing of this Holy Mother Cow in your heart and life. She can become a loyal companion for you as she knows who you are and what you've been through. You have already learnt so much. Take this time now to make notes in your journal about today's meditation, so you can learn from your progress.

Each morning, take time to meditate for Five to Ten minutes. Call in the Great Cosmic Cow Mother, to be with you in your life, so you can keep feeling loved and nurtured. Any time something happens to you, you can handle it in a different way and begin to feel more able to relax and cope better. Make any notes or observations in your journel to help you learn from it.

Now bring your awareness back to yourself and your body. Have a good start to the day, and Thank the Cow Mother for being in your life. Bless Be, Namaste.

Full Moon Journey With The Swan

Find yourself in a nice comfortable place that you can sit with your back straight. Or you can also lie down completely flat on your back with a pillow under your knees and a pillow underneath your head. Have a blanket close by so you can cover yourself and feel warm.

Create a sacred space by firstly burning some sage to cleanse and purify the room and yourself. Breath in the sage and make a positive intention to connect with your soul on this Full moon night. Light some white candles and burn some Frankincense incense. Pray to Brighde to come and be with you to help you heal your wounds and to let go of anything that no longer serves you. This is your time to receive and go deep within yourself.

Begin by focusing on your breathing. Take three deep breaths in through your nose and out through your mouth. Become aware of any tension in your body and give the intention to release it down through the floor and the earth. Feel yourself heavy in your body and begin to quiet your mind by imaging your thoughts are like clouds in the sky, just drifting by. You are entering a deep state of relaxation. Bring your awareness t your heart by breathing into your heart three times, feel your heart chakra opening up. This is the home of your soul and it is here that you will be making the journey home.

Imagine yourself at the side of a huge beautiful lake where there are many graceful swans swimming in the water. Close your eyes and feel love in your heart sending out a message to a swan that you wish to be with them. Now ask one of them to be your guide for your soul's journey. For a moment you are deep in connection, feeling impulses going out to the swans, and then before you know it, one of them has responded to you and is flapping it's wings bringing you out of that deep connection. You open your eyes, surprised and happy at the same time that you have been able to connect telepathically with the swan. You feel a great loving energy sweep over you as the swan descends upon you opening its expansive wings as an encouragement to jump on its back. Without hesitation, you quickly jump on its' back.

You are thrilled that you have made this special connection with your swan. You begin to ascend upwards, going over a huge lake and coming into the clouds. You are holding on with a strong grip, until you realise that you can relax a little better now. You are relieved and you let your hand drop down onto the swan's neck and you feel yourself dosing, falling into a nourishing light sleep. You begin dreaming of a beautiful land, where the sun is shining and there are rainbows in the sky. It is a magical place where all your worries are lifted off and you can be, simply be the way you want to be without any aggression or pretense. Instead you begin to relax and trust the deep feelings that are surfacing as the swan flies below the clouds. Then suddenly you are surrounded by mists and just can't see anything, you close your eyes and enter the mystery of the unknown.

Then when you open your eyes the mists have cleared and now you can see a large lake surrounded by rolling hills. You also notice some little natural springs of water flowing out into a river. You feel like you have entered a very special place, as your heart starts to beat faster as you feel yourself getting excited knowing that you are getting closer to source. Your swan dives down and make out a shape in the landscape of a bigger swan, and you know that you are in the right place. You are getting close to the land now, and you can make out natural houses made from earth and an unusual building that looks like a temple with swans decorated on it. You notice the building is all made out of clay and straw and beautiful made into the shape of a swan. There are soft feathers imprinted on the door and as you open it, you see hundreds of snow drops, lovely white flowers with little bell shaped flower heads. All around the room, there are furry animal skins and white fluffy pillows for you to lie down on.

Your swan is no where to be seen now, but you are greeted by stunning young maidens dressed in white flowing outfits, with swan feather necklaces and unusual markings on their skin. 'Welcome to the Swan Temple, Your Journey home to your soul has begun! Please lie down, we bring many gifts of healing to you.' You gratefully lie down and feel all your emotions beginning to release and you sense the touch of light feathers brushing you down all over your body. You feel yourself gently drifting off into sleep. You feel like you are being rocked gently and images begin to appear, just like being in a dream, unfolding before you. It seems like lifetimes ago, showing you where you lived and events that took place. All these memories are being cleansed and released as levels of painful memories surface to be healed on a soul level. You are in the Swan haven, and can feel the swan's wings wrapping around you, keeping you safe, as karmic lessons are revealed to you. You continue to breathe as these lessons are transcended into the light and you can see your swan calling to you to jump on its' back again as it carries you into the summer lands to a place of deep healing in the other world. Here you receive the divine light of the Feminine and all your wounds in your sacral chakra that are ready are being attended to, very gently, with what you are able to handle at this time. You are lying down now in a bundle of swan's feathers and holy water is being poured over your sacral chakra and your heart chakra to deepen the level of healing. As you breath in and out, memories of birth, of giving birth, of being pregnant with child come pouring out as you go deeper into yourself and release all that you have been carrying to the Swan Mother who is helping you to let go.

Take this time now to go into a place of stillness, to find your centre and know that you are loved and with the Goddess. The Great Mother loves and accepts you for all that you are. You surrender with grace and just allow all the hurt that might come flooding out. Tears may start to well in your eyes and drop down your face. Just allow yourself to feel and surrender to the divine love and healing that is flowing through you. You give great thanks and you feel a wonderful warmth in your belly that now feels full and nurtured. Your heart is lighter and you feel more relaxed.

Your beautiful swan is carrying you back to this world now and gentle drops you back into your body. You begin to feel your feet and hands and you allow yourself to stretch. You reach your arms as high as you can. You feel like yawning and let your jaw drop. Take time now to reflect on your journey that you just made, and what happened for you. Drink a glass of water to ground yourself. Take a moment to write down your experience.

Brighde's Swan
Aquarell on watercolor paper
Isabella Weber

Crone Wolf
Oil Pastel on paper
Isabella Weber

Journey with the Crone Wolf

Make yourself comfortable by lying down. Have some pillows and a blanket over you. Light some candles and burn some of your favourite incense. Begin by taking deep breaths in through your nose and out through your mouth and begin to imagine your thoughts are like clouds in the sky drifting by and allow yourself to begin to feel more and more deeply relaxed. Bring your awareness to your body and notice if there is any tension in any areas. Once you notice the tension in that area, imagine your breath is going to that part of your body and as you breath out, it is releasing, easing, and softening the tension. All that has been tight can now begin to soften and become filled with oxygen, leaving the body feeling heavy on the floor. Imagine the earth below you like a magnet, Mother earth is drawing out even more tension, all you have to do is simply hand everything over to Mother earth, all the stress. Surrender your body, your pain and all that you have been through and begin to let go.

Imagine yourself going down the stairs leaving this world behind, as you go down each stair, you are relaxing even more deeply, until you reach the bottom of the stairs and you see a door in front of you with your name in gold letters. You open the door and you are startled by the sound of drumming. You are completely surrounded in mists, it appears to be early morning and you can see the sun is starting to stream down through the mists. That is how you can make out the shape of trees and you can smell the scent of burning wood. You know there is a campfire happening somewhere.

The sound of the drumming is getting louder and louder and it is drawing you to follow the sound to find the source. You make your way slowly through the woods, walking over bracken, leaves and branches that are crackling as you walk over them. You are aware that somehow you are not alone, you feel like you are being watched, and yet somehow it feels safe, like someone is looking out for you. As you feel yourself getting closer to the drumming, there is a gap in the trees and you can barely make out as you turn around that you have entered a sacred grove of trees that are surrounding you completely. The mist is still thick, but the light from the sun is beginning to strengthen and you can make out these openings that are clearing, where you notice that there are mountains behind the trees.

You begin to feel tired and stop for a while to gather your breath and to take in the surroundings. As you sit down and let out a sigh of relief, the drumming intensifies and now you really need to lie down completely. It is as though the drumming is taking you into a deep trance state and you can hardly keep your eyes open. You let go and start to feel waves of energy flooding your entire body. You breath deeply and are completely knocked out by a second wave of energy that is even stronger that the first. This really is powerful. Then as you are barely conscious, you make out the sound of running feet and you know instinctively that someone or something is coming.

Suddenly you are taken over by this surge of fear, maybe they are coming for you, you start to think. You are taken over by this fear that your life is in danger, your heart starts to pound and you that you must open your eyes and stand up and face whatever it is that is coming for you. As you pull yourself together and gather your courage, you stand up and open your eyes to realise that you are surrounded by wolves who have come in great numbers to met you. You are firstly taken aback, but as you begin to relax, you turn around and look each wolf in the eye and know that something very special is about to happen. You are in awe of these wolves, their beauty, the stunning colours of their fur. Each one has unique markings. You notice the age difference as well as some them appear older with more furry white patches and wider eyes. There are young ones as well, who you know would take you down in an instant. They howled and it sends a huge shiver down your spine. This is a test of some kind, and it is time to act.

You begin walking around the circle, showing the wolves that you have released your fears and are now ready to meet with one of them. Which one is it going to be? Who is going to be your guide and walk between the worlds with you? Who is going to be the one that shows you your path and opens the way forward. These thoughts are moving through your head and your whole body is shivering and shaking at the same time. You can feel yourself wanting to growl and run with the wolves. Suddenly it happens, and one slender wolf with incredible yellow eyes charges towards you and you jump up to meet it! Entangled together, you roll and begin playing. Its' wet tongue licks your face covering you with its saliva. The wolf pack disperses and another howl shrieks though the air. The dawn has lifted and the sun is fully present in the sky shining its light on you both. You climb on its back and it takes you on a journey deep into the woods. Everything is flashing by so fast that you can't make anything out. The wind is blowing strongly on your face and you close your eyes, holding onto your wolf's fur for dear life.

Everything begins to slow down and you feel your whole body aching. You hear the sound of rushing water, it sounds like a waterfall and as you open your eyes, you see a crystal clear pool of water below a huge waterfall, and your wolf is tugging you to look.

'Look down my little one. Look down into the waters and see yourself as you truly area. I Call to the Grandmother, she who holds the wisdom of the ages. See her sprinkling her wisdom like snowflakes falling down above you. It feels like soft snow and you are swimming, healing and rolling in her snowy stardust. You recall the old ways of surviving, how the ancients lived. Now my little one, drink now, drink the water for it is filled with her loving wisdom and it will help heal your body and your spirit to become one. One with all of creation, for you are love. And this my little one is for you. Your wolf presses its paws on your hands and you receive a gift that is something you have always wanted. Your heart opens with loving gratitude. You drink as much water as you can. Intoxicated, you are overcome with the energies and can not keep your eyes open.

You fall into a deep sleep and the sound of drumming comes back and everything is in fast forward as once more you are riding on your wolf's back. Before you know it, you are again conscious of your body, your back, your neck and shoulders. You need to move and stretch. Take some deep breaths, you begin to notice the room you are lying in. Drink a glass of water to ground yourself, and reflect and write down your experiences.

Soul Healing Journey With The Unicorn

Prepare yourself for meditation. Make yourself comfortable with your back straight on a chair, or lie down on a floor with pillows and a blanket. Imagine yourself like a tree, sending your roots down through the floor and into the earth, traveling further down into the soil, into the levels of tree roots. Going down reaching the mineral kingdom, the rocks, the layers of the earth, see yourself going further and further all the way down to the liquid gases, through the fires of the earth, until you reach the centre of Mother Earth. See Mother Earths centre as a glowing ball of violet light filled with loving energy. Breath that all the way up through the layers of the earth, rising all the way up through the floor and up through your feet, moving up your legs all the way to your heart centre. Feel your heart opening to receiving this loving energy of Mother Earth.

Feel your heart filling up as it opens. Breath three deep breaths and see the violet light completely immersing yourself like a violet flame. Now imagine a fishing line moving up from your heart centre, rising up through your throat, through the centre of your head, moving up from the top of your head, all the way up through the ceiling into the sky. Traveling through the clouds, moving beyond the clouds into the atmosphere of the earth. Now moving beyond the earth, going all the way into the universe, moving through the planets and the sun, going far far away to the brightest star you can imagine. See yourself reaching this loving bright white star and you are the star are expanding as you join together and burst with energy. All this loving energy is now traveling all the way down like the speed of lightning. You are now moving all the way down your line of white light, past the planets and the sun, down towards the earth, then into the atmosphere of the earth. Now moving down through the clouds into the sky, all the way down into the building, through the ceiling, traveling down to the top of your head, filling the top of your head, your crown chakra with this liquid loving light. Feel your crown chakra expand and open up. Take deep breaths as this loving energy moves down through your head, into your throat, then into your heart. Once it is in your heart, it merges with the energy of mother earth. Take three deep breaths as your heart opens even more and this divine energy moves through your entire body, filling you up.

Now imagine from your heart the earth in front of you as a beautiful ball of blue light. Allow your mouth to open and make a sound and chant aaahhhhhhhhhhh, allow more sounds to come out of your mouth. With this sound comes healing light that is surrounding Mother Earth, and sending this healing light to all those people , plants and animals who need healing. Just allow yourself to feel calm and settle back into your body. Breath deeply again and bring your awareness to your heart.

Magical Unicorn
Aquarell on watercolor paper
Isabella Weber

Imagine yourself in a beautiful place beside the sea, or in the mountains or a forest. This is a sacred place that you can retreat from the world. This is your healing sanctuary, a place you can visit to connect with the world of spirit. As you explore this place, you are already beginning to feel more relaxed and at ease. You feel a strong desire to connect with your soul and to deepen healing of karmic patterns related to family and situations in your life. It would be helpful for you to receive more insights into your life's purpose, understanding the reasons that you are here on this earth. You feel your heart full with these desires and you call for help. You call for a loving friend in spirit, a companion who knows you on every level. A companion who has chosen to help you on your journey this lifetime. Here comes your unicorn, your beloved spirit guide in the heavenly realms who hears your call, and is coming down from the sky to be with you. You feel your heart is filled with questions as your unicorn comes closer. You notice the colour of your unicorn, its wings and its glowing horn. As you hold out your hand to receive and meet it. You can now let go of your shyness, you maybe meeting each other for the first time. It feels like a reunion of loving lost friends coming back together. You feel great joy and recognition in your heart. Your unicorn wraps its loving wings around you and you feel yourself connected, receiving its love and healing. You look up in the sky and a beautiful rainbow appears as a sign from above. Doors are opening.

You journey together with your unicorn as it takes you to places that help you to see things about your life in a different way. You may wish to visit work, your love life, or your family situation. Just simply whisper your intention to your unicorn and together you ride to revisit situations, events that happened in the past, so you can see the behaviours, the feelings of the people involved and how you reacted. Take this time now to feel what it is that you need to know, your unicorn will help you. With its love and healing horn, it can help you to be at ease and accept certain lessons that are lessons for you to learn this lifetime. It is helping you to know yourself. Every night when you sleep you can call to your unicorn and it can continue to help you heal in your sleep as these deep patterns become released and you feel more capable of coping with them. Your unicorn will help you see solutions coming to you, that you weren't able to before. Your unicorn is helping you to heal your inner child, and bring back your innocence. It will help you to begin to see your life again through the eyes of a child. Take time to play and have fun together. Enjoy your special magical time together. Then you will know when to come back, and to feel your body again, to feel yourself grounded. Take your time and drink a glass of water. Reflect on what you have been shown with your unicorn and write it in your journal.

After working with these meditations, you will notice that certain ones will speak to you more, so go with those that call you and begin a daily practice which will help strengthen and deepen your connection with Brighde's Sacred Animals.

Chapter 4

Creating A Sacred Healing Flame Brighde Oil

Image - Isabella Weber

Image - Isabella Weber

On Saturday 26th of February in East Sussex a group of women gathered together to share and connect with the Goddess Brighde. We all felt tired and in need of rejuvenation, with the cold winter dragging on, it was time to receive Brighde's healing and light.

A Goddess alter was created on the floor to represent Brighde in all her aspects; as Maiden, Lover, Mother, and Crone. Also her four elements were represented in the directions. The East, for Brighid's fire, her eternal flame, taken from Kildare Ireland, held in the Goddess temple in Glastonbury and combined with the light of Hiroshima in Japan. This flame is lit every Wednesday at 6pm to remember Brighde's healing light sending it out into the world to help all the people, animals and mother earth who need healing. In the South are Brighde's healing waters taken from the Holy White and Red Springs in Glastonbury. In the West is Brighid of the Earth, in her green cloak, ancient mother Brigantia of this land of England. She was once, in the Celtic times, worshipped by Pagans before Christianity. She stands at the crossroads between the two faiths for she is also a Saint. In Ireland she is Brigid of Kildare and the second most popular saint after Patrick. She has opened a doorway between these two expressions of spirituality. Reading her story as Saint Brigit, she was rumoured to be born in a doorway between the worlds. With that comes her mythical creatures; the Healing Unicorn who ascends from the heavenly realms to bring healing to one's soul. Alongside her unicorn is the Phoenix, a great bird that rises from the ashes bringing change and transformation. Offerings to the Goddess Brighde were placed on the alter to represent her qualities and invite her presence.

To begin the ceremony a meditation invoking Brighde was made.

Mediation to Invoke the Goddess Brighde

Lying down comfortably on the floor, or sitting on a chair with your back straight, begin to focus on your breathing. Breathing in through your nose and out through your mouth. Take the time to feel your body and release any tension through your breath, taking a deep breath in and then out through your mouth. Imagine your feet are like roots of a tree going all the way down into the floor, into the earth all the way down through the molten lava of mother earth, travelling to the centre of mother earth. Seeing Mother Earth as a huge ball of violet light and feel your roots connect to her centre as she welcomes you home with love. Feel all the baggage, burdens you have been carrying over the winter and trust it is time, that you can hand them over to mother earth, she wants to take it from you. Breath into your heart and imagine your heart opening up to receive her love. Feeling your heart beat connecting to her heart beat. Feel like you are releasing into her love and light. Breath her energy up through the roots of your tree into your body. Now breath into your heart and imagine yourself going into nature, into a beautiful place with green rolling hills, it may feel like you are travelling back to ancient England a time where the earth was full of vibrant soft green grass and plenty of nature all around you. Here you find a little babbling spring and you can hear the birds singing and there are butterflies all around you, You feel the sun shining down on you, filling you with warmth and energy as you lie down on the grass to rest, a gentle breeze blows on your cheek, and all your thoughts are like clouds in the sky just drifting by.

We call to Brighde, Brigit, Bride, maiden goddess, come and be with us as a young girl, full of innocence, purity, playfulness. Help us to remember what it was like when we were children without a care in the world, simply wishing to play and explore life as an adventure. Come with your healing unicorn who brings out our inner child and helps us to release pain in our heart from family and relationships that have affected our lives. Imagine Brigit as a young sweet girl, smiling and playing, she is there with a swan in the water stroking its beautiful neck, and watching how it's wings expand as it takes a huge leap out of the water and flies into the sky. 'You too can be like the swan and reclaim your maiden self it all it's beauty. Feel my light renewing you and bringing to life your inner child. Have fun come play with me and my unicorn will help you to remember the good times.' Brigit whispers in your ear and memories from childhood come flooding back, helping you to let go and feel her positive light healing deep inside. 'Come with me as I take you to my healing Fires!' Brigit beckons and you follow her as she leads you to a cave with a huge fire burning in the centre. 'Here are my Fires of inspiration, of healing, my fires of the forge of transforming smith craft. As you look above you, you see a huge bird. 'Don't be afraid this is my phoenix who guards my fires, she has come to welcome you to my source of purification. Take your time now to release energies inside of you that no longer serve you, dance with my fires, feel your internal fires burning inside of you, inside your soul.'

You are mesmerised by Brigit's fires and you dance and release into her flames all the negative experiences and thoughts and challenges you have been having, you hand it over to the flames and the flames drink it up like liquid honey, the flames are hungry for your anger, your emotions, for your exhaustion, your challenges. Sit by the fire and feel the warmth of Brigit's healing flames, warming your heart and soothing your soul. You feel refreshed and renewed, Brigit is calling you now to connect with your lover, as the phoenix disappears into the light, suddenly you are alone in the cave and there appears a snake. This is your snake of power of love of passion, the enchantress calls you to remember your body and become charmed, open your heart to receive the love of the fire of passion that burns within, let the snake come into your life. Don't be afraid, it will help you to shed a skin that holds you back from experiencing more of the pleasures of life, the excitement and joy that you can feel, Look into the snakes eyes and remember who you are! Seeing the snake can awaken fears and memories held within, however you are feeling trust that your experience with the snake is helping you to heal deep inside, trust Brigit is showing you the way.

Soon the snake is gone and the cave calls you to walk through it's gateways and you hear the sound of rushing water and are called to explore the cave further. Soon you see an opening and come to the source of a huge reservoir of water. It is sparkling and full of life, you dive in and drink it up, releasing all your fears into water, feel the healing that the water brings. Brigit's waters carry great wisdom that is there in your womb, helping you to connect to your higher self and feel compassion, liberating your emotions and all you wish to let go of. Take this time now to experience the healing waters.

Feel your connection to her healing waters and take your time and feel your way in. Take this time to let go of the past and awaken your self love and compassion for all the lessons in your life. Feel the water softening and easing your journey.

Coming out of the waters you are welcomed by Brigit the Mother as she covers you with a huge warm cloak and wraps you up. She takes you through a doorway and welcomes you to her home. Brigit of the hearth of the Home, the mother that provides all the you need, She is there for you, holding you, loving you unconditionally, helping you to receive all that you need. Her home is beautiful and exactly how you had imagined it to be. You feel comfortable and safe, it's a lovely place. You look outside the window and you see Brigit's cows with the red ears, and you can hear them mooing in the distance. Brigit brings out wholesome food, it's time to eat she says and has laid out the table for you with all the fruits and vegetables cooked in a most delicious way. Here is some fresh milk that I picked up this morning from our darling Mother Cow, she produces the most divine milk. Thanking Brigit you drink down the milk, you can not believe the taste, it tastes so good. Oh! You feel relieved and nurtured and loved. All your cares and worries have drifted away, you are in the arms of the Divine Mother.

After your meal, Brigit takes you outside and invites you to lie on the ground on the soft green grass. You take this time to connect with mother earth and feel her loving energy grounding and supporting you through these changing times. How nice to be able to simply lie down and rest on the earth on the body of the goddess, you take your time and enter a deep healing sleep.

Upon awakening you are greeted by an old wise women who knows your name, she knows everything about you. Firstly you are surprised and then as you look into her face and you see the wrinkles of time and age, there is gentleness and kindness in her eyes, you know you can trust this wise women. 'I am Brigit the crone, I walk between the worlds, come I have much to show you about your life and I have a guardian to help protect you.' You can not believe your eyes, you trust and follow this old women who is draped in a cloak from head to toe. She has a walking stick for her legs are heavy and she walks slowly but strong with a will that you wouldn't wish to test. Suddenly you hear the sound of a wolf cry and before you appears a wolf with bright eyes. 'Don't be afraid, this is your test, call your wolf to you, she is here to help you walk between the worlds and look after you.' You hold out your hand, to over come your fear and the wolf comes closer and licks your hand, you stroke its fur, it feels so soft and warm, a deep bond has formed. 'What is your name my friend.' listen carefully your wolf will speak it's name or give you a message that you need to hear.'

You turn to thank this wise women for such a wonderful gift, as you turn she is gone, there is no one there and it is getting dark, it is just you and the wolf. The wind begins to blow strong and you can feel the breeze more like a blizzard, you look up and it is Brigit of Air, coming down from the night sky, bringing the light to show you the way home. A vision in white she is stunning with silver hair, glowing with beauty. 'Time to come home she says, time to return to this world.' She holds out her hand and you take it, and before you know it magically she has brought you back into this room, into your body, into yourself. All you remember is what you need to remember. Great healing has taken place, Brigit has brought you home, to where you need to be right now. Thank you Brigit, beautiful Goddess, thank you for your healing presence, thank you for being all that you are, for being you. Bless you Brigit as we make the Sacred Healing oils in your name, bless these oils with your loving energy, they are made in your name. Thank you Brigit. Bless it Be.

Coming back into the room, we are taken deeply by our experiences with Brigit and a sharing takes place, as we listen to each other's stories.

Image - Isabella Weber

Making of the Brighde Oil

All the ingredients and a bottle of Almond Oil is prepared as we now make the oils. Follow the recipe below, pour 10ml of Almond oil into a clean bottle, then adding the drops of the essential oil as laid out in the recipe below. Once you have made your bottle and added the drops, take your hands and feel Brigit's healing light flowing through them and bless the bottle with love and thank Brighde. You have made your oil. Enjoy it.

Brighde Flame Healing Oil

Smells and Properties of Love & Healing

Carrier Oil: Sweet Almond Oil

Drops:	**Cedarwood**	**3 drops**
	Neroli Light	**3 drops**
	Rosemary	**2 drops**
	Benzoin	**3 drops**

Cedarwood Virginia: is a holy wood and can be used in all ritual work. It is protective and particularly suitable for attuning to nature spirits. It opens the intuitive channels, bringing forth compassion, humility and prosperity. It is purifying and helps to dispel negative energies and attract good spirits. It also protects the seeker on his/her spiritual journey or vision quest.

This clean smelling, balsamic oil does not only help calm and balance energy, but also promotes spirituality, while helping to clear the respiratory system of excess phlegm and catarrh. It sorts out urinary tract infections, as well as bladder and kidney disorders, while improving oily skin and clearing up dandruff. Cedarwood oil's great benefit lies in its ability to calm and sooth nerves. It relieves skin and hair problems and is important in easing conditions of a respiratory nature. It also clears rheumatism and arthritis.

Neroli Light: has a very relaxing effect on the body and mind, relieving muscle spasms and calming heart palpitations. It has a wonderful rejuvenating and regenerative effect on the skin. It helps to prevent ugly scarring and fights stretch marks. It is also known as 'orange blossom' and it takes about 1000 lbs. of orange blossoms to make 1 lb. of Neroli oil. The name is said to have originated from the Italian princess, Anne-Marie de la Tremoille (Countess of Nerola) who used the oil as a perfume and to scent her bathwater and gloves. It is still an ingredient for making traditional smelling eau-de-cologne.

Neroli is an ideal oil to use in all kinds of love potions, lotions or amulets. It opens and attunes the heart chakra to the vibration of love. It can be used to get in touch with one's feminine energy and sensuality.

It is a wonderful oil to use in tantric rituals and all acts of pleasure to celebrate the Goddess.
Orange petals are often associated with marriage, purity and brides, as brides traditionally wore orange buds in their hair.
Neroli oil is very relaxing and can relieve chronic anxiety, depression, fear, shock and stress and its calming effect can also be beneficial to the digestive tract. It can be used for intestinal spasms, colitis and diarrhoea.
It helps insomnia, and as one of the essential oils with the most sedative effects and is also effective in calming heart palpitations, treating headaches, neuralgia and vertigo. It can help when a patient is convalescing and is a good general tonic.
On the skin, neroli oil can help to regenerate skin cells and is a rejuvenating oil useful to prevent scar tissue, promote a smoother skin and aid broken capillaries.

Benzoin: is a resinous oil and has a great calming and uplifting effect on the mind. It helps to comfort the sad and lonely, while boosting circulation and easing respiratory disorders. At the same time it boosts the skin's elasticity, while calming redness, itchiness and irritation.
The profuse smoke of Benzoin provides excellent 'substance' in which spirits may manifest. Its sumptuous sweet scent is suitable for use in love magic as it will stimulate sensual perception and open the heart chakra. It lends itself well to use in aphrodisiac potions and incense blends. It can help the mind to let go of painful emotions, past grievances and resentment, Benzoin may attune the heart chakra to the vibration of love as a balance between give and take. In Java, shamans use it for shape shifting to take on the animal bodies of their spirit allies.
Benzoin oil's greatest benefit lies in that it has a calming effect on the nervous and digestive systems, a warming effect on circulation problems and a toning effect on the respiratory tract. It also boosts the pancreas, which in turns helps digestion, and is thought to be involved in controlling blood sugar, which makes it valuable for sufferers of diabetes.
The effect it has on the skin is to improve elasticity, helping cracked skin, while aiding the healing of sores and wounds and at the same time reducing redness, irritation and itching.

Rosemary: is a crisp and clean smelling essential oil that is great for stimulating the brain, improving memory and mental clarity, while helping with a variety of congested respiratory tract problems, stiff muscles and coldness as well as boosting the liver and gall bladder. It is also used for improving hair and scalp health. It has a long and intricate history as a magical herb. It is strongly protective and purifying, warding off evil influences and witches and cleansing the atmosphere of bad energies. It has been used to burn in sick-rooms too and can be used in healing rituals to help to dispel the demons of disease. It can protect against bad dreams and all manner of evil influences. Rosemary can support the student by helping him or her memorise teachings and to concentrate on the work. It is used at funerals to keep the memory of the departed alive. At weddings it is used to remember the timeless bond of the souls and the love that has brought the couple together. Rosemary gives vigour, strength, courage and mental clarity.

It helps with headaches, migraines, neuralgia, mental fatigue and nervous exhaustion and the antiseptic action of rosemary oil is especially suitable for intestinal infections and diarrhoea, easing colitis, dyspepsia, flatulence, hepatic disorders and jaundice and relieving pain associated with rheumatism, arthritis, muscular pain and gout. It also helps for arteriosclerosis, palpitations, poor circulation and varicose veins. The diuretic properties of rosemary oil are useful with reducing water retention during menstruation, and also with obesity and cellulite.

On the respiratory system, it is effective for asthma, bronchitis, catarrh, sinus and whooping cough. Because of its astringent action, it is also effective for countering sagging skin. Its stimulating action benefits scalp disorders and encourages hair growth.

On the skin, it helps to ease congestion, puffiness and swelling and can also be used for acne, dermatitis and eczema, but a very popular use of this oil is the use in hair care products, as it has a pronounced positive effect on the health of the hair and scalp. It increases the circulation to the scalp and is therefore also effective for promoting hair growth.

For more informatin on Essential Oils and their properties please contact Star Child, in Glastonbury.

Image - Isabella Weber

An Alternative Recipe that you can also try:

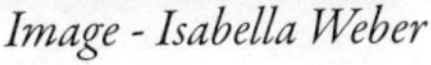
Image - Isabella Weber

Brighid Anointing Oil by Brighde Priestess Sarah Arkle 2011

Smells and Properties of the Spring

Carrier Oil: 10ml Sweet Almond Oil

Drops:	**Juniper**	**3 drops**
	Cedarwood	**2 drops**
	Pine	**2 drops**
	Violet	**3 drops**

Juniper: Removes illness, promotes healing, purification.

Cedarwood: *See page 82*

Pine: Cleansing, health and energy, protection, purification and divination.

Violet: Increases happiness, prevents accidents and soothes the nerves, fragrance brings comfort. It is used in love healing spells.

Blessed Be, Sarah

How to Use it

Evening Ritual

Take a bath and fill it with a handful of sea salts to cleanse and relax you. Light your favourite candles to enhance your mood. Afterwards massage the oil onto your body, breathing in the scents of the aromatherapy. Feel your muscles soaking it in, and gently work your way over your stomach to your back, just go wherever you feel your body would like to be massaged.

Morning Riutal

When you wake up, light a candle at your alter and call Brigit in to bless you with her healing. Place the oil on your temple points, your wrists, your sacral tummy or on your feet, or wherever you feel guided to, this is your sacred Brigit Healing Oil!

If you enjoyed making this oil, there are more rituals and ceremonial making of Brighde craft in the one year correspondence training.

Chapter 5

The Brighde Retreat and Priestess of Brighde Training

Image courtesy of Steve Dixson

Image courtesy of Marion Van Eupen

In February 2007 on my final year of my Priestess of Avalon training with Kathy, I dedicated as a Priestess of Brighde on the Brighde Goddess retreat. We had a wonderful time making Bridie Dolls, walking the landscape of Avalon and celebrating her as a goddess in all her aspects as Maiden, Mother, Lover and Crone. I discovered her connection to water, as a goddess of holy springs and wells. I felt her very powerfully in The White Spring, which is a stone well house and reservoir of water that flows out of a cave system under the Tor and runs down a small valley that flows into the well house. It was here that I discovered a painting of Brighde made by Wendy Andrews of this goddess with a huge red and golden fire light coming out of her heart chakra. Above her head is a beautiful swan flying, I really connected to her through this image and felt her flames of light rising in my heart. I also experienced Brighde as a shepherdess, where another painting of her is there with a flock of sheep standing tall with gold colour in her hair. This was such a strong image to me, it spoke of her purity and golden light, there she stood strong as a shepherdess, looking after the land and her sheep. I experienced a special connection to Brighde then and there and wished to be her Healer Priestess,. I felt guided to bring her light and energy into the world.

That year after the retreat, my healing practice started in London and I continued to light her flame every Wednesday evening at 6pm and began to enjoy creative projects and practising goddess spirituality. She had touch me so much that the following year I rededicated in 2008 as a Priestess again and enjoyed honouring her in my life, asking for continued strength and courage to be her light in the world and to grow and learn more. That was a really special time for me and I felt her light and inspiration really coming through as I began to trust her more and the path she was showing me.

Later that year Kathy was guided to hand the Brighde retreat over to Priestesses who were wanting to continue the tradition and lineage of keeping Brighde's light alive. I was called to take this on with another lady, Marion Van Eupen, from Holland who now lives in Glastonbury. Together we ran the Sacred Blessings Brighde Retreat for three years.

Here is one of the retreat participant's experiences:

Brighde's Sacred Blessing Retreat
Glastonbury UK
January 29th to February 1st 2009

At Imbolc, the first stirrings of Spring, a small band of women, seven in all, gathered in the Miracles Room in a secluded courtyard in the centre of Glastonbury. From this special place we experienced the safety and intimacy to welcome Brigit the Maiden, the Bringer of Light, to get to know Brigid the Goddess, Bridie of the Isles, Briganttia of this Land, and to acknowledge and hold dear the inspirational Bridie within ourselves.

We were greeted with fragrant incense and a wonderful circular altar to Bridget, honouring Her in all Her directions and in all Her aspects, Maiden, Lover, Mother and Crone. The offerings for the altar were mostly in white; swan, unicorn, snake, shells, stones, water chalice, and of course clouds of white "swan" feathers. As we called in Bridie together, we felt that the energy of Her blessings was warmly feminine, springing from a deep well, though light in touch.

Participating in ages old country traditions, we made Bridie dolls with pretty fabric scraps, wools, beads and buttons. The results were quite arresting. We also interlaced Brigid crosses with willow, to place at our doors and windows to avert the "evil eye". Adorning the loose, silky threads - so like a unicorn's mane, with plaits, knots and ribbons, we fashioned healing girdles, each perfectly symbolic for the individual craftswoman.

Communing with Her through the elements, we took trips on on Bridgit's land. At the White Springs we held a candlelit ceremony to meet Brigit through water, the ancient Goddess spirit living at the heart of the spring. At Chalice well, we offered, each in turn to the other, the waters from the Red and White springs, bestowing for one another specific Bridie Blessings.

We also walked the hillside of the Holy Thorn, resting our dolls in the yoni before carrying them, well sheltered against the biting North East winds, to Bridie's Mound. Here we called in Bridie with songs and our own poetry recitations. After nurturing the land with ewes milk, we received welcome nourishment from delicious, barley honey cookies baked for us by Marion.

The visualisations and journeyings were a treat. Laying down with our heads to the altar, we glided to Avalon on a river barge. Parting the mists we went to meet Bridget in all Her temples and rooms, accompanied by Her wondrous creatures, unicorn, swan and phoenix and giving us Her messages of transformation and new beginnings.

By the final day our connection had so deepened that in joyful spirit, dressed in ceremonial robes, headdesses and veils, we made the short walk to the Goddess Temple. The atmosphere was blissful as we spoke our dedications to Brighde and received Her gifts, with the sweet understanding that She knew and loved the secrets of our hearts.

On our last afternoon together we had time for more handicraft. Weaving with wool, over and under a cross of birch twigs, we made Bridie eyes. As we wove we brought together the strands of our wonderful experience. We spoke of the meaning of this unique time together, knowing that we had forged a significant relationship with Bridie and that She would be always with us.

Thank you to Isabella and Marion, amazing Brigit Priestesses, for a very special retreat, for holding us in your "Bridie" arms and enabling us to see, and come close to beautiful Brigit in all Her loving faces.

Rita Lewis

Image courtesy of Marion Van Eupen

The future of the retreat is changing now and evolving to a one year training course to Dedicate as a Priestess of Brighde. All the details of the training in Glastonbury with Marion Van Eupen are on The Goddess Temple website *www.goddesstemple.co.uk*

I too have been inspired to offer a One Year Priest/Priestess of Brighde Correspondence Course

Becoming a Priestess/Priest of Brighde by Exploring the Wheel of Brigit-Ana and experiencing Brighde's Medicine.

This course is designed for those who wish to develop a closer relationship with the Goddess Brighde and her ancient land. It is intended to develop yourself in your own country and with your own local environment and community. It is teaching you how to develop Priestess/Priest skills and create your path as a Priestess/Priest of Brighde.

During the course you will learn about the Goddess Brighde, her lineage and also Brighde the Patron Saint. You will be introduced to her qualities as a Fire and Water Goddess and how that will have an impact on your spiritual practices. You may yearn for knowledge and practise of the old celtic times. This course will teach you how to connect to the ancient land of England Brigit-Ana. You will learn through celebrating and understanding the festivals how Brighde can help deepen your connection to the land and Mother Earth.

The course is divided into 8 weekends spread across the Celtic year starting in February at Imbolc. It will involve self practice meditations and creative assignments. You may choose to spend time alone or gather in small groups to share the experiences celebrating each ceremony throughout the wheel of the year.

You may be drawn to Brighde to help encourage your creativity and inspiration. You may have a great love of poetry and the spoken word. You may work with children or young adults. As a triple Goddess Brighde holds three aspects of womanhood, the maiden, mother and crone. Throughout the course we will explore where you are in your womanhood/manhood and what aspect Brighde can help bring alive or temper.

Brighde is also the Goddess of Alchemy, soul healing and transformation. As a smithcraft she teaches you how to forge metal with fire symbolically this is the same way she works spiritually helping you to clear out any dross in your life that isn't serving you. Brighde shows you how to make empowered changes that do serve you, even if you didn't know it at the time.

Brighde is also the Patron Goddess of many animals; her lover snake, her crone wolf, her mother cow with red ears, her swan maiden, as well as her magical unicorn and transformational phoenix. During the course you will be introduced to each animal and you will be guided to connect to each one through meditation; developing your own personal relationship to each one as the course develops through the year.

Lesson One: Finding your Maiden Self

This lesson begins your journey in celebrating Brighde's light at Imbolc. She appears as the maiden helping you to find your joy and innocence to nurture your inner child. Your creative task is to make your own Bridie doll and explore your maiden self. You will be introduced to her Magical Unicorn through meditation which will help you to heal deep rooted family patterns and bring healing in for you on a soul level.

Lesson Two: Awakening your Inner Fires; Reclaiming your Power

This lesson introduces you to the power of Brighde's fires at the Spring Equinox. This celebration balances the light and dark within the self and the land. You will learn how to make your own Brigit candle and discover the healing practices of Brighde's perpetual flame. You will be introduced to Brighde as a Patron Saint, her life and legacy. You will also meet her transformational Phoenix through meditation, which will assist you in burning away what no longer serves you to then opening the gateways to your personal power. You will learn about Brighde as a Warrior Goddess and be able to make your own Goddess Poi Flags and practice the art of Poi.

Lesson Three: Reuniting Love; Shedding Skins

In this lesson you learn to celebrate Beltane the festival of Love. It is a time when the veils between the two worlds are thin. Brighde appears to all your fears and inhibitions, how can you go deeper into loving yourself and others? We will look at relationships and explore where you feel weak or strong. Your creative task is to make a white snake wand to activate your mystical abilities. You will also learn about your Kundalini and begin meditation and breathing practices to harness your sexual/creative energy.

Lesson Four: Unleashing the Flow; Experiencing Brighde's waters

Lesson Four coincides with the celebration of Summer Solstice. It is a time of expansion and opening to the flow of life to take you where you need to be in your life. During this lesson you will create a water purification ceremony to wash away old patterns that no longer serve you. It is time to explore local wells or visit your nearest water hole. You will meet Brighde's beautiful swans in meditation flying with them to Avalon, where you will cross the waters of her mysterious lake. Your creative task is to start making your ceremonial clothes for your dedication. What are your words for Brighde, where is she showing you the flow in your life?

(During this time you will prepare your dedication to come to Glastonbury before the Goddess conference starts for your ceremony to dedicate to Brighde)

Lesson Five: Embracing Brighde as Mother

During this lesson you will learn about the nurturing time of the celebration of the Lammas festival; which is a thanks giving ceremony for all you have received in your life. Your creative task is to bake bread in the form of Goddess shapes and share the fruits of your abundance with friends and family. You will meet Brighde's magical cow with red ears in meditation. You will learn about Saint Brigid and how she always gave everything she had to the poor, then all her supplies were magically replenished, there was no scarcity . Time will be given for you to explore your mother patterns and abundance. Practices will be given to show you how to start healing them.

Lesson Six: Brighde and Community

This lesson coincides with Autumn Equinox, when the light and dark meet once more, this time the light is fading. It's time to reflect and call Brighde in as Earth Mother to weave her magic into your life in a practical way; grounding your dedication. We will explore community projects, working abroad in developing countries with women sharing creative skills and abilities. You will create your own regular meditation practice to connect with Brighde in whatever aspect she appears. Your creative task is to plant a tree that symbolises your connection with Brighde.

Lesson Seven: Entering the Darkness; Journeying between the worlds

During this lesson you will learn how to take time to remember your loved ones, those who have crossed over before you. This is the celebration of Samhain; the festival of the Souls. This weekend you will meet Brighde as Crone, the wise one who holds you in dark places of fear and depression. What is masking your emotions, your shadow self? Journey with Brighde's wolf in meditation and walk between the worlds in safety and love. It is time to connect with your ancestors and honour them. Your creative task is to make a Brighde body oil that will keep you warm and energised to last through the winter.

Lesson Eight: Finding Peace and Stillness

There is so much chaos at certain times of the year. This lesson teaches the important challenge to take time out and be still. This lesson can also be is a celebration of Winter Solstise; the shortest day of the year. The light is bright and soft as the sun sets earlier and darkness takes over the early evenings. It's time to share stories and sit by the fire feeling Brighde's warmth. Your creative task is to make a Bridie Eyes and as you make them weave your stories into them. They may be dreams of the future, or stories from the past, make them count. Meditate on finding your inner peace and stillness no matter what is going on around you. Call in Brighde of air to bring you gifts of clarity and wisdom to trust the path of how your Priestess\Priest is unfolding knowing you have found your way.

The course can be adjusted for different countries, starting in September for Australia, New Zealand, Asia Pacific and the Southern Hemisphere.

You will receive a Full Course Manual with all information and outlines for the weekends.

Correspondence will take place via emails, and scheduled phone calls or Skype sessions can be arranged. Follow up will take place on completion of creative tasks and preparation for your dedication.

For more details and an application pack please email: isabelle@lotushealingcentre.co.uk
or view www.lotushealingcentre.co.uk

Image courtesy of Marion Van Eupen

Interview with Kathy Jones Thursday 10th February 2011

Isabella: When did the Goddess Brighde first come into your life?

Kathy: A long time ago in the 1980's when I first began looking for the Goddess's in this country, I noticed there wasn't anything local. The first impressions I had of Glastonbury when you came here were all the stories, the legends were all male. As I read more I disocvered Morgan Le Fey, Queen Guinivere and then there was archealogical references to St Brigit who had come here from Ireland and had stayed on Bridie's Mound. What astounded me was the stong presence of her nature in Glastonbury. When I began to look more into the landscape I discovered the shape of a swan, and that her presences was in the land she was here physically. Wieryall hill, The Tor was her body outstretched in the land. St Brigit was also a sun goddess, she brought in the light from the dark winter. She has been with me a long time.

Isabella: How did you start the First Brighde Retreat? What inspired you?

Kathy: I began creating workshops on helping women to heal themselves through making Bridie Dolls and it grew from there. Brighde to me is an aspect of the main Goddess. It was a reason to celebrate her and bring her to life. The first retreat began in 2005, and there wasn't a dedication ceremony in place to be a Priestess of Brighde, that was to come later. The idea was to bring people together to introduce them to the Goddess of this land. What inspired me about Brighde is her creamy loving energy, her ability to create a spark of life; to bring creation into the land after winter. In 2006 I had a big group of Dutch women from Holland come over and it was through working with them that they wanted to dedicate to be a Brighde Priestess to make a dedication to Brighde to love and serve her. It was then that it became a Goddess retreat Initiation into her energy whereby I embodied the spirit of Brighde and brought that through for people who were on the retreat.

Isabella: What is your connection with St Brighde and the Isle of Iona?

Kathy: I found a book written by a lady called Iona, published in 1929 called the Story of Saint Brigid. It is in this story that Saint Brigid goes to the Isle of Iona and whilst she is there she goes through what is called a 'Gael' it is like a sacred cave or doorway and when she passed through it, she ended up in Bethlehem with Mother Mary and Joesph and she was Mother Mary's Midwife and baby Jesus's wet nurse. This is a very special story which is why I am doing a retreat in Iona to honour Brigid's journey there. That is why she is called 'Mary of the Gael'.

Isabella: What started the Brighde Priestess Tradition?

Kathy: I think what started it, was I was developing the Esoteric Soul Healing Training and through that I learnt to call Brighde's healing energy into my body. This started a loving relationship that I felt could be passed on to other women and men who also felt that calling to celebrate and bring Brighde's light deeper into their lives. The more that I have called the Goddess into my life the more she shows me different things. After the 2008 Brighde retreat my life was changing and I felt a desire to develop new aspects of the goddess, it felt right to hand it over to Priestess's who felt guided to continue the tradition. As you experience it yourself Brighde is always growing and changing and now the retreat is evolving into a year long Priestess training and that feels right.

Isabella: Thank you Kathy for your time and sharing this sacred experience of your relationship with Brighde. I wish you a wonderful retreat in Iona in May this year. Goddess Blessings

Kathy has spent the last 30 years living in Glastonbury, also known as the Isle of Avalon, learning the ways of the Goddess in this ancient and sacred place.

She is a Priestess of Avalon and has played a key role in bringing back awareness of the Goddess into Glastonbury. She is the author of several well-loved Goddess books, including: In the Nature of Avalon, The Goddess in Glastonbury, Spinning the Wheel of Ana, On Finding Treasure, Breast Cancer: Hanging on by a Red Thread and Chiron in Labrys (all Ariadne Publications).

Kathy is a teacher of priestesses, offering with Erin McCauliff a three-year training to become a Priestess of Avalon. She is co-founder of the Glastonbury Goddess Temple and organiser of the fabulous Glastonbury Goddess conference. Please view her website *www.kathyjones.co.uk*

Images courtesy of Marion Van Eupen

Chapter 6

Brighde Priestesses

Priest/ess Gateway, Glastonbury Tor

Image courtesy of Steve Dixson

Priestess Marion Van Eupen

Here is a selection of work written by inspired Brighde Priestesses who have done the training in Glastonbury on the Brighde retreat.

Priestess Marion Van Eupen

Brighid, My kind of Goddess

To understand my journey with Brighid, you have to know a bit of my background. I was brought up Catholic with a strong connection to Mary. It was She that I talked and prayed to, rather than God or Jesus, who felt too high up or distant for me. I also grew up in a happy and creative family, with a father who was spiritual in a intellectual way and a great poet and a mother who was spiritual in a practical way and a enthusiastic nature guide. Growing up I was very much involved in church, mainly doing children services, motivated to have two lovely children. And on the other hand we as a family were very much orientated on Great Britain, we were what you could call Anglophiles with a strong interest in the old and Celtic ways.

When I started my priestess training in 2003 I was looking into the background of the Goddesses on the Dutch Wheel of the Year and found there was an immense amount of information about Brighid or Brighde or Brigantia. I was drawn to Her immediately and found it fascinating that She had been a saint as well as being a Goddess. Very much like Mary in my point of view. And on top of that She was called Mary of the Gael as well. A journey had began!

It's not very easy to explain why you are attracted or identify yourself with a certain deity. But at the same time I can give you so many reasons why I was attracted to Brighid. It's the promise of a new Spring; the snowdrops popping their heads through the snow, it's the healing of the inner child; it's Her inspiration, poetry, songs; it's Her tradition in the British culture: the legends, the stories, the making of Bridie Dolls, the Brighid Cross, the Brighid Eye, Healing Girdle; it's Her Hearth Fire; the Alchemy of the Soul; Her animals, the Swan, Snake, Cow and Wolf... The list could go on and on...

I think the biggest calling for me became clear, when I did the Sacred Brighde Blessings Retreat in 2005 with Kathy Jones. We were asked to let Her talk to us and write poetry and this is what I wrote:

Brighid-Ana,

my motherland is calling me.

I hear her voice in everyday
signs

in smells, dreams and
thoughts that come to me.

Brighid-Ana,

my soul belongs to you;

your hills, rocks and sacred
stones,

your mantle of fields of green,

form the shapes of my body;

your clear streams and wells,

your dark lakes and wide rivers,

is the blood flowing through my
veins;

your stormy skies and scents of
peat fires,

your white rushing clouds through
summer skies,

is the air that fills my lungs;

your strong minded people,

the fire in your songs and
traditions,

is the spirit of my being.

Brighid-Ana,

take me in you loving arms

for I am your strayed child

and you are my mother,

Brighid-Ana.

She is Brighid-Ana, Brigantia, Goddess of the Land, of the British Isles. She lives in the Land, the Land where I belonged. But I did live in The Netherlands with my family then. And although we went on holiday to Her Land every year at least one time, it didn't look that we were going to move to England soon.

Another thing I got through during that Retreat was that I had to bring Her out into the world. So I started setting up the Brighid retreat (Brigida Her-innerd) in The Netherlands. In the very south of The Netherlands, in a little village called Noorbeek, there is a strong Saint Brigida culture. She was brought there when monks from Ireland came to Belgium and the Netherlands and took Her worship with them. In Noorbeek you can find a Brigida Well, a Brigida church and chapel, a street and an Inn called after Her. Even the inn keeper is called Brigitte and she has statues, Brighid crosses and lots of information to read about Brigida in the inn. There is also a whole culture with legends about Her especially about the protection and healing of cattle.

Each Imbolc the farmers still come and bring branches into the Brigida Church to be blessed and then the will touch their cows with the branches so they will be protected in the coming year. And at Beltane time the young men of the village will get to the forest to get a very large pine tree. That is stripped down except of the very top (the size of a Christmas tree) and brought on a horse drawn vehicle into the village. The young women stand on the side of the roads and welcome the young men and their pine tree, what then will be erected next to the church... This tree is called the Brigida tree.

It was very clear that I had to run the Dutch Brighid Retreat in this village in the Netherlands. So I did and initiated some very special priestesses of Brigida over the years. In this context

I do want to mention my sisters Evelien Brighid van Meerveld, who I 'baptised' Brighid at the time of the retreat and Lida van de Water, who now runs the Dutch Brighid Retreat in Noorbeek. Because since then (and through personal circumstances) I did answer the call of Brigantia and moved to Glastonbury in 2009.

This came much sooner than ever could have been expected, but all happened in a magical and held way. It wasn't very easy, but I knew She was there with me, guiding and guarding me. I know this through things that happen to me all the time. For instance, Kathy asked people to take over the Brighde Retreat in Glastonbury and I'm was running the yearly Retreat together with Isabella Weber! And when I was asked to move out of my room, I found a lovely house in St. Brides Close, where I live now exploring my journey a priestess of Brigantia further day by day. Now I am offering the Priestess of Brighde Training in Glastonbury.

There is much to be grateful for since Brighid came into my life. And I do celebrate Her in many ways, one of them I want to share with you. It's the Lady Awaken prayer from Kathy Jones, which I (with permission) adapted into a prayer for Brighid:

Brighid Prayer

Brighid, awaken my fiery spirit

Brighid, open my vision through
time and space

Brighid, be in my breath, words,
songs and in all my actions

Brighid, fill my heart from
your sacred source

Brighid, sooth my emotions and
heal my body

Brighid, bless my sexuality and
inspire my creativity

and as I walk on your Green
Mantle, ground me in your love

Bright Blessings,

Marion van Eupen
Priestess of Brigantia

Sacred Brighde Priestess Training, Glastonbury:
www.brighdesblessingsretreat.blogspot.com

Brigida Her-innerd, The Netherlands:
www.avenahar.blogspot.com/2010/12/agenda-2011.html

Priestess Heather Upfield

The Queens Litanies

Introduction

When Isabella Weber called for contributions to this book, I submitted the final poem in what has been a short series of 'The Queen of ...' Litany-Poems, which use the device of the Queens in Court Cards of a standard playing card pack, along with the playing card Suits. For years I have been fascinated by playing cards with the colourful representations of the Court Cards (King, Queen and Jack) who are always depicted in 15th century costume and the simple design of the number cards of the four Suits (Hearts, Clubs, Diamonds, Spades). My poetic theme started with a poem at Lammas 2009, as a particular request, and I then developed this over the ensuing months. These later poems became a number of devotional Litanies, still using the Queen/Suit format. Isabella asked for an explanation and previous examples to augment the final contribution and I am happy to unfold the story of how they came about.

Playing Cards

My study of the history of playing cards found that they appear to have originated in China, but earliest records in Europe date to about 1370 (1). While the four Suits we know today were standardised in the 19th century, prior to that, the Spaniards used Cups, Clubs, Coins and Swords; the French used Hearts, Clubs, Diamonds and Spades; while the Germans used Acorns, Leaves, Bells and Hearts - they even used Unicorns, Dogs, Rabbits and Apes, plus other more wild examples (2). While there is some evidence for the Suits representing different strata of society, in the spirit of anything goes, it occurred to me that there was no limit on what could be a Suit: a pack of Bottles, Swans, Spoons and Hooks - anything at all.

The Tarot

Contrary to popular belief, Tarot cards are not recorded until nearly 100 years after playing cards, in the 1450s. It is generally thought that they were originally another form of playing card - indeed some games used a pack comprising the standard 52 card pack plus all the Tarot cards. It was some time before they were used solely for divinatory purposes.

1. The International Playing-Card Society, History of Playing-Cards. Available from: http://i-p-c-s.org/history.html - Accessed 2 March 2011

2. A Brief History of Playing Cards. Available from: www.essortment.com/all/historycardspl_rncs.htm - Accessed 8 February 2011

The standard Tarot Card pack comprises the Major Arcana (pictorial cards denoting figures such as The Empress, The Lovers, The Fool etc) plus 4 Suits, known as the Minor Arcana, which are usually Cups, Staves, Coins and Swords (3). However, there are many variations - the Merlin Tarot pack, for example, uses Fishes, Beasts, Birds and Snakes (4).

Oracle Cards

In a similar vein, over the centuries, the Tarot Cards have also developed into pictorial Oracle Cards, for example Angel Cards, where random selection of a card gives the querant an answer or direction. In this tradition, and in a way coincidentally running parallel to my theme, Ceri Norman, from Wales, has produced a wonderful and inspirational set of Brighid Oracle Cards, with beautiful and exquisite designs, which will be available in Summer 2011 (5). These really are stunning and something to treasure.

The Queens

Having studied the Suits of a pack, I started looking closely at the Court Cards and in particular the Queens and their representation. The depictions are common to all packs, and show the same attributes. For example, in playing cards, the Queen of Spades always holds a flower and a sceptre. In the Tarot pack, The Queen of Cups (or Fishes in the Merlin) is always associated with water, Venus and the lunar cycles. Each Queen, whether playing card or Tarot, has a specific design or meaning.

So what is it about Queens? I leave aside the issues surrounding monarchical succession, dominance, privilege and capricious rulers. Instead I focus on the positive qualities. For me the essence of 'Queen' epitomises the Feminine - the perfect woman: strong and soft, the warrior and pacifier, hard-working and industrious; the intelligent, articulate female, who leads and inspires, protects and cares, lover and wife, mother and aunt, regal and plain, just and loyal, temporal and divine.

My own Queens of inspiration are St Mary, Mother of God, known variously as Queen of Heaven, Queen of Sorrows, Queen of Angels and Queen of the Rosary. Another is St Margaret, Queen of Scots, beatified in the 11th Century, in the four-fold veneration of Queen, Mother, Wife and Saint - the only woman ever to have been thus canonised. And Brighid herself, the Queen of Fire and Light, earthy and realistic - "whose throne is a daisy surrounded by bees" (6) - in her triple reign of Queen of the Hearth, Queen of Poetry and Queen of Healing.

3. Mann, A T (1993). The Elements of the Tarot, Element Books Ltd, Longmead

4. Stewart, R J (2002). The Merlin Tarot, Element, London

5. Norman, C (2011). Brighid Oracle Cards, The Tarot Media Company - Summer 2011

6. From 'The Summer Solstice' in Upfield, H (2009) Songs of the Oystercatcher, available from Brighid - Goddess and Saint site at www.brighid.org.uk

Priestess Heather Upfield

The Litany-Poems

I had all this in mind when I was asked by a colleague for 'an earth mother' poem for a book he was writing on Pregnancy in Mental Health (due for publication in 2011). What emerged was the first in a series of "The Queen Of..." Poems, entitled 'The Partum Queens'. Using the Queens/Suits device, where there is the possibility of a Suit being anything at all, my Queens are associated with imaginary playing card Suits that reflect the essence of conception, pregnancy, delivery and birth. It is written in the first person, illustrating the beauty of pregnancy, in the context of a pregnant woman where there are mental health concerns.

The Partum Queens

I am the Queen of Shells
In the soft interior of my fallopian tubes
My baby forms as a seeded pearl
I am the Queen of Pools
In the warm waters of my womb
Floats my baby in the making
I am the Queen of Orchards
My belly swells like a juicy plum
Around my baby as she grows
I am the Queen of Corridors
Down my dark and spongy vagina
My baby travels to the light
I am the Queen of Secrets
Of a hidden cavern deep within
My body is a sacred space
I am the Queen of Clasps
I hold together the present and the future
My body links them to the past
I am the Queen of Keys
I am pregnant and invincible
My body unlocks the mystery of life
I am the Queen of Ribbons
I am beautiful in my pregnancy
My body weaves the fabric of the world

Heather Upfield 2009

Over the months, I was inspired by Brighid to explore this theme and developed some minor 'Queen Of ...' poems. Eventually, I discovered that the poems were becoming more devotional and were taking the form of a Litany. This is a simple prayer, which very often forms a list to be recited: for example the Litany of the Saints, which lists by name over 50 saints (7). The first Queen/Suits Litany-Poem was dedicated to St Bride, who has been my inspiration, guide and guardian, for so many years. It is titled 'Capellae Sanctae Brigid Reginae' - 'The Queens of St Bride's Chapel'.

7. The St Andrew Daily Missal (1943), Geo E J Coldwell, London (written/edited by Dom Gaspar Lefebvre OSB of the Abbey of St André, Lophen near Bruges, Belgium)

I have put the poem in a Mediaeval context, as most of the 90+ chapels dedicated to Bride in Scotland were in use up to the Reformation in the 15th century. The Litany incorporates some Latin, as during this period, it was used universally in the Church. Moving from writing in the first person (the "I am the Queen of ..." poems), this became a paeon of praise to Bride, with a different emphasis: "You are the Queen of ...". By again using the Queens/Suits device, it expresses the powerful spirit of Bride as Saint, where the chapel itself is a manifestation of her religious devotion.

Capellae Sanctae Brigid Reginae
(The Queens of St Bride's Chapel)

St Bride of Kilbride, be with us

You are the Queen of Service
Of the ceaseless ministry to the Divine
You are the Queen of Stones
Of the Column and Narthex, Nave and Crypt
You are the Queen of Eden
Of the heavenly garden and the hallowed ground
You are the Queen of Symbols
Of the Altar and Crozier and the sacred Cross
You are the Queen of Cloisters
Of silent worship and contemplative prayer
You are the Queen of Choirs
Of the hymn of praise and the psalm of sorrow
You are the Queen of Smoke
Of candles and incense, perfume and light
You are the Queen of Water
Of the Piscina, Baptistry, and Stoup
You are the Queen of Chapels
Of the Chancel and Sanctuary, Vigil and Veil

Spécie tua, et pulchritúdine tua inténde, próspere procéde, et regna. Propter veritátem, et mansuetúdinem, et justítiam: et dedúcet te mirabíliter déxtera tua
With thy comeliness and thy beauty set out, proceed prosperously, and reign. Because of truth, and meekness, and justice: and thy right hand shall conduct thee wonderfully

Gradual Psalm: Psalm XLIV 5 from the First Mass: Dilexisti, for St Bride's Day (7)

Heather Upfield 2010

The final Litany-Poem in this series (and my original contribution) is dedicated to blessed Brighid herself, as Ancient British Goddess and the Queen of Fire and Light. It is entitled 'The Brighid Canticle - the 19 Queens'. Nineteen is a number sacred to Brighid, and the 19 Queens and their Suits represent all the regular symbols of Brighid (the mantle, forge, girdle, etc) plus others that are my own. I wanted this poem to be a one-stop shop of references to Brighid, in the true form of the Litany. As a Canticle it may be sung - in whatever way you choose!

I also felt it important to recognise Brighid in a Scottish context, where she is to be seen in the landscape across the length and breadth of the mainland and the isles (Hebrides). I reference Scottish associations with fishing and the sea (wherever you are in Scotland you are never more than 70 miles from the sea) and Bride's traditional place in the fishing communities (8). I also reference the traditional Celtic prayers surrounding the mundane and domestic order of the day.

There is some Auld Scots (otherwise known as Lallans, Braid Scots or the Doric) in the use of the word 'Quine'. Linguistically, this word for a young woman, is also where we get the word 'queen' from in English. In the context of the poem, I reference Brighid as the 'Queen of Quines' - in other words, the 'Queen of Women', but also by extension, the 'Queen of Queens'. I have also included the Gàidhlig (Scots Gaelic) word for Oystercatcher: 'Gille-Brìghde'. This means quite literally 'Servant of Brighid', and bless this bonny wee bird, it serves her so well!

The Brighid Canticle - The 19 Queens

Sweet Brighde: you are the Circle of our lives and the Square of our understanding. May your light guide us, your energy empower us and your spirit sustain us. You are here now.

You are the Queen of Quines
from the young girl to the old woman, the midwife and foster mother, nursemaid and aunt.
You are the Queen of Petals
of the rush of Snowdrops at Oimelc, the milky Dandelion of Spring and the Attar Rose of Summer.
You are the Queen of Lyrics
of poetic inspiration, of insight and intuition, of word and verse, rhythm and metre.
You are the Queen of Feathers
of your totem Swan and your servant Oystercatcher (Gille-Brìghde).
You are the Queen of Looms
of the spinster and spider, of webbing and weaving, the warp and the weft.
You are the Queen of Tails
of your wondrous creatures - your sheep and cows and your guardian wolf.

8. McNeill, M (1959). The Silver Bough, Vol 2, A Calendar of Scottish National Festivals - Candlemas to Harvest Home, William Macmillan, Glasgow

You are the Queen of Cloaks
of embracing and enfolding, of the greening of the land and the mantle on the Sun.
You are the Queen of Isles
of your Hebrides, of the mysterious veil between the beach and the sea.
You are the Queen of Anvils
of the fiery arrow and the forge, of melting and smelting, the smith and the iron.
You are the Queen of Cascades
of the gushing fountain of healing water that splits the rock and bathes the soul.
You are the Queen of Coils
of the snake and spiral, labyrinth and maze, of the going in and the coming out.
You are the Queen of Altars
of the hallowed and the sanctified, the sacred silence and the interior prayer.
You are the Queen of Spans
of bridges and crossings, fords and ferries, from side to side, from one world to the next.
You are the Queen of Aprons
of the house and the hearth, the broom and the skillet, and the domestic round of the diurnal day.
You are the Queen of Fathoms
of the salt deeps and whirlpools, of fishers and fisheries, the creel and the kelp.
You are the Queen of Sashes
of the belt and girdle, of the drawing together, of the ties that bind.
You are the Queen of Campaniles
of ringing the changes, of the proud peal of carillons and the sombre tolling of the sacristan's bell.
You are the Queen of Honey
of your daughter bees, the hive and the purpose and the mellifluous sweetness of life.
You are the Queen of Candles
of the February flame which pierces the dark, and the glimmer of hope which flickers in the fire.

Give thanks.

Heather Upfield, January 2011

Heather Upfield lives and works in the West of Scotland and was dedicated as a Priestess of Brighid, on St Bride's Mound in Glastonbury, at Lammas full moon 2010. As well as writing devotional poems, she has been researching and recording sites in Scotland dedicated to St Bride/Brighid for a number of years. Titled 'In the Footprints of Brighid" the spreadsheets of this research are to be found at Paul Williment's beautiful site Brighid: Goddess and Saint at brighid.org.uk/scotland_footprints.html. Her cycle of devotional poems - 'Songs of the Oystercatcher' - dedicated to Brighid in the spirit of the 8 Festivals, is also available from the same site. Heather's latest work is a booklet compiling information about the 30 Bridie churches in Scotland still consecrated and functioning, entitled 'Circle of Bright Light'. *Heather Upfield can be contacted at brihdein@live.co.uk*

Priestess Iona Eveson

Priestess Iona Eveson

Hello, my name is Iona and I was born in the town of Worcester in England to two Welsh Parents. I was not brought up with any 'Religious' training but, as a child, would communicate wordlessly with the wonderful energy above me. I remember that she would speak to me in the silence of our communication and I would feel and see silent golden bubbles of laughter flowing up to her followed by a feeling that I was one with her. As a child, this relationship was so natural and I never questioned who she was and therefore grew up always listening to my heart, and always trusting my inner voice.

One day visiting my Aunt in Glastonbury, I found out there was a temple just off the High Street and on my second visit was asked by the Melissa if I was going to do the Priestess training, I told her no, and went home. That night my energies bounced off the walls and ceiling of the bedroom all night until, out of pure fatigue, I shouted "OK, I'll do the course" and everything went quiet - and that is how I came to do the first and Second Spiral's of the Priestess of the Goddess training in Glastonbury with Erin Mc Cauliff in 2007 and 2008. In 2009 I did Kathy Jones Esoteric Soul Healing Course with which I am still growing as a healer and was also called that year to do Isabelle and Marion's Bridie Retreat during which time Bridie gave me the name of the healing centre she wanted me to begin. In 2010 I began the third Spiral with Kathy Jones in Glastonbury to become a Priestess of Avalon. And now in my fifth year of training I am guided to do Sally's 'Spiritual Self Development Course' knowing that this will complete the training I have been guided to do by the Goddess of Glastonbury. I do feel that once this coming years training is completed I will be ready to serve the Lady of Avalon in the way she wishes me to serve her.

My Experience with Brigantia

Brigantia came to me just after the beginning of the first Spiral and I recognised her name from Kathy's book but did not know who she was. I began to feel her walking within me checking her boundaries as she went. She appeared to have great strength within her – especially in her legs and feet which never seemed to stop walking. Her energies flowed out over the Summerland's, the Tor, and beyond. I quickly began to enjoy her presence until after approx 3 weeks her steps became lighter and she began to fade away. It was then that the 'Song of Brigantia' began to flow into my mind and I knew it was coming from her, her strength came through every word – it truly was a wonderful experience.

I have never been able to think of the 'Song of Brigantia' as mine – it truly did come from this timeless strong feminine energy called Brigantia.

My experiences with Bridie

At the meeting of the First Spiral with Erin McCauliff in 2007 I knew nothing of Priestesses, of the Goddess, or of the Lady of Avalon. I had just begun to experience Brigantia but once I became aware of Bridie she always came to me as a swan. Many times I felt her swan nature filling my aura until I became the swan – I now know this is called shape shifting. I also feel very connected to her snake – another connection to the other world.

For our first Imbolc Ceremony in 2007 Erin our teacher took us to Brides mound, a mystical mound that lies west of the town and has much history attached to it. It was here for the first time I saw Bridie's wolf circling our ceremonial circle and saw a huge flame arising from out of the centre of it. It was only later that I learned that this was Bridie's flame and realised I had also seen this hovering over the water in her well. I was so delighted to be aware of her wolf who stayed until the Spring Equinox energies began to flow in - in fact I felt overjoyed with the whole experience.

From the beginning of Imbolc I felt the inner maiden – a delightful pure child mirrored by the young garlanded girls who took part in the Imbolc Ceremony that was held in the temple that year. I felt so connected with these wonderful energies which flowed in and around me for the whole of Imbolc. As Imbolc progressed so the maiden developed until she became a brilliant pure shining light. At that time I realised that this was the light that Christianity had claimed for itself and called it 'Mother Mary, Mother of God'.

Each time I do Esoteric Soul Healing I call in Bridie and I always experience a swirl of energy that flows over and around me and my client. I have always seen this to be Bridie's green cloak of Healing and Protection.

It is my experience that Bridie is the innocent Maiden, the purest of White Light, and Holder of the Sacred Flame. For me these are all aspects of the light within each woman's Soul.

A Song written by Brighde Priestess Iona

Song of Brigantia
(Imbolc)

I have called men to me since ancient times
For I am the Spirit of Celtic Lands
I am the breath they breathed as I wove their worlds
And shaped them in my fires.

I am the dark womb out of which all things arise
And in time must return to this sacred darkness
But now, as this first light begins to stir
I call to you to come to me.

Come bathe in my healing waters
Purify yourself in my sacred flame
Hear the songs on my breath as I breathe you
Let your quickening begin.

Let the power of the white rod inspire you
As the Caillach loosens her hold
Open yourself to this time of Imbolc
And I will Birth you into this Sacred Land.

Priestess Moana

Ode to Autumn

Whispering your arrival through leaves of favourite trees,
Slow - but then suddenly free to be who you really are,
Fallen burnt orange foliage,
Swarming swallows,
People in sorrow
Trees -

Cold sunshine,
Warm moonshine,
And beyond the veils, the chanting of priestesses remains suspended in the autumn mist of mountainside.

For the autumn air is punctuated by the arctic unicorn's breathe,
Forewarning an arrival,
Snow Queen and her knowing wolves,
Remember.....

Raven bird is your black swan,
Aloof black butterfly,
Black deer fawn.

For the start of autumn is when the willow weeps the end of seasons,
Shield us from the cries and laments with your gentle howling reasons.

Priestess Moana 2011

In life, a woman can become a priestess, a healer, a sorceress or a prophetess...some women are all of these things and more. I favour the priestess path over all others for it brings with it a rich inner landscape with quiet moments of devotion in prayer, where everything becomes nature's metaphor. A sanctuary touched only by the light of the goddess, where no word is wasted, no light is too weak, no darkness takes root.

Priestess Moana - Image courtesy of Aude Dorian

As a Priestess of Brighde I find my spiritual home in the Brighde temple of her inner landscape, it is a place of sacred beauty, of serenity and divine geometry. It is here that my prayer echoes the vortex of the Fibonacci sequence, and I receive gifts from the goddess in return. To me these are the gifts of the mysteries: beams of light from within.

At first I discovered Brighide's barren landscape, then it became like a field filled with all the flowers of the world.

My prayer as a Priestess of Brighde, is like the justice of the righteous, the valour of the brave, reflecting the passion of lovers, and it will always be part of the tapestry of the sacred feminine's collective unconscious.

Moana is from London and dedicated as a Priestess of Brighde on the Sacred Blessings Brighde Retreat in Glastonbury, at Imbolc 2011. As a human rights campaigner for over a decade, Moana has worked on a range of issues, including Guantanamo Bay prisoners, child soldiers, trafficked people, women's rights and children accused of witchcraft in Africa, in addition to working on environmental and ocean protection campaigns. She also works in conflict zones to highlight human right abuses.

Moana enjoys writing metaphysical poetry inspired by the Goddess Brighde and training in Tribal Gothic Fusion Belly Dancing with Tree Russell. As a keen surfer, Moana also loves the ocean and everything in it!

Isabella's Biography

Isabella was born in Australia and grew up in nature and developed strong intuitive gifts for connecting with mother earth. She trained as an artist and further developed her career in Thailand by studying Buddhism. Her true spiritual calling came on travels in India, where she discovered her Reiki Master by chance and the universe guided her through coincidences and experiences all the way along her journey. She came to England eleven years ago and began her training and development of her psychic gifts and healing abilities. Over a four year period she spent learning the ancient ways of healing by training in Soul Rescue and spiritual traditions of Priestess practices in Avalon, Glastonbury. This, combined with body massage therapy and Indonesian massage, developed her unique style of healing massage also incorporating Aruyvedic creative healing methods; lymphatic drainage techniques to heal mind body and soul. She has a busy London practice and has been running Holistic healing retreats over the last five years in Russia, Cyprus, Greece, Sweden, Copenhagen, Turkey and Spain.

www.lotushealingcentre.co.uk

Ancestral Spiritual Healing

Ancestral spiritual healing is a very specialised and developed form of healing which offers transformation for the person through clearing ingrained ancestral patterns inherited from families and passed down through generations. These ingrained patterns can create trauma, drama and limitations in a persons life which holds them back from doing what they really want to be doing and living the life they want to be living.

Dakini Goddess Wisdom Cards

Dakini is the supreme embodiment of highest wisdom and the most potent manifestation of feminine divinity in Tibetan Buddhism. This wisdom card reading helps one to be lead through life's turning points. Dakini in Sanskrit means Sky Dancer, with sky connoting creativity and potentiality. The Tibetan Buddhism Dakini cards represents the individual journey of our spirit that wishes to push through toward enlightenment. The Dakini cards are symbolic and may appear wrathful, but the wrath is aimed at her/our own states of anger, greed and delusion. The Goddess wisdom seeks to cut out and transform these negative traits and great determination is needed. Buddhist Dakini severs the heads of beings who are none other than her own demons. Hers is not a glorification of anger and violence but a transformation of it. The Tantric Dakini Oracle reading provides ancient symbolic representations of the female principles of intuitive wisdom. The Dakinis are the guardians of the deeper mysteries of the self, and it is through them that the secrets of inner transformation are opened.

Spiritual Reflexology

This treatment combines intuitive reading with healing and relaxation. It works on balancing the physical aspects of the body and helps to release emotional ingrained patterns.

Indonesian Massage

This unique massage works on clearing the energy lines with deep palm compression as a fundamental technique. The massage starts dry and then a warming oil is applied. This powerful massage will leave you uplifted and recharged and is an effective way to relieve stress.

Pregnancy Massage

Pregnancy Massage incorporates Creative Healing as an excellent way of clearing the body of congestion; optimising lymphatic drainage. This is necessary for a gentle birth as the joints and muscles of the lower back, sacrum and coccyx need to be functionally mobile and clear of congestion. When muscles and ligaments return to their normal state, they automatically become supple and elastic.

Testimonials

The womb is a holy place. The womb is also a place where many, maybe most, women are hurt without knowing it. The womb is a place where memories are stored, also memories from every time we have been hurt in our deepest femininity, in our feminine essence.

I knew this when I came to the Goddess workshop Isabella Weber had in Malmö in March. I knew it but had obviously not really understood it. Until she led us in to the deepest feminine and made us feel and heal. There, I realised how hurt I was, how frozen I was, and how much it affected my life. Even though I had done a lot of personal development job all my life, also with focus on feminine subjects.

I have met a lot of skilled teachers and facilitators in my life. Meeting Isabella was not only meeting a teacher but also meeting a Sister Goddess who made me remember, recognize and deeply feel, the goddess in myself. Through wonderful guided meditations and inner journeys, music, movement, sound, the elements, symbols and cards she helped us re-connect to Mother Earth, to our Goddess linage and our selves, to heal our inner wounds and to see our own journey clearer.

If you have felt stuck in your life the energies starts to move, and if they already were moving, they flow more easily. In all parts of your life.

I think the work Isabella Weber is doing is something every woman and men need, it is easy and simple, yet so powerful and full of beauty, joy and sacredness.
Irene Ahlberg

Ancestral Spirit Clearing Healing Sessions

With Isabella I had an ancestral spirit clearing session. it was the most liberating and relaxing thing I've ever done. I feel lighter, happier and filled with positive light. Thank you!
Dana Flynn

Isabella you are just great, I felt you touched the right points and I tell you I feel much more secure and free at the same time. Like I told you I felt that you would be helpful to me 20 days ago. I really feel like a feather thanks. Love
Zeynep

This session was a unique experience for me to understand several things underneath my body and soul, and of course the universe. I am grateful to you, to life which led me to this session. Thanks a lot for this journey to my incarnation.
Seyda

I am continuously learning and experiencing new opportunities for a fuller life. Joining Isabella's session was just another new step for me. During the meditation part I have strongly experienced that I am receiving wonderful support from existence.
Veet

Isabella became a stream of love and energy for me and my baby. Her healing Reiki energy and nurturing ways cocooned us in health and happiness, and gave me a great lesson in what a mother should be. With her guidence, I took charge of myself and incorporated her wisdom and knowledge into my everyday life.
Elspeth

First Session-I was not aware after we started with meditation. I woke up just before the end only feeling I had a light headache. Second Session-I was aware but I was not sure what was happening. Now I feel myself more relaxed and something is changing deeply. Thank you
Gagm

Pregnancy massage

Isabelle is the most genius guru for any mummy-to-be. She practices and preaches Dr Gowri Motha's treatments, nutritional advice and birthing plan. She started doing my pregnancy massage at around 3 months (the earliest they advise) and is now giving me an all-round programme for a fabulous pregnancy.
Patricia

Following her guidence I changed my diet, avoiding wheat, and ate very healthily; took the vitamins and herbal teas she suggested and had a fortnightly wonderful session of creative healing with Isabella Weber she is brilliant!. Following this regime meant I had an amazingly healthy
and enjoyable pregnancy.
Normandie

I was given 6 sessions of massage as a birthday present and this included a combination of Indonesian, Aromatherapy and Reflexology. The massage was conducted in a very professional way and left me feeling very calm and relaxed and with a great sense of wellbeing and my body felt very
good. All my aches and pains disappeared instantly.
Karen